"He Said Die. I say No!"

"He Said Die.
I say No!"

Lesley A Sehli

Printed in Great Britain by Biddles Books
King's Lynn, Norfolk PE32 1SF

Contents

Acknowledgements. viii
Author's Note.. ix

PART 1 Top Gun

The Adventure Begins 3
Black Pearl 9
The King and I 13
Murder Most Foul... 21
1980-1985 Exciting Times 23
    First Placement – based in Thailand. 23
    Second Placement – based in Philippines. 23
    Child – Mestizo 23
    Rock a bye baby... 25
    Third Placement – Based in Frankfurt Mayday! Mayday! 27
1985-1996 Women Power in the Desert!.. 31
Underworld.. 35
Human Rights Violations against Women!... 37
Four Secrets. 39
    Rape without Justice 39
    Women of the Night... 42
    Please Don't Leave Us! 44
    Termination of the Innocents 48
Headhunted. 51
Desert Storm... 53
Headhunted Again.. 63
The City of Gold 67
Sleepless in Seattle... 71
1997–2000 Top Gun... 77
Sandstorm (Haboub) 81
Miss Lesley, Help Me!!!... 85
Guilty or Not Guilty... 109

PART 2 – Spider's Web

Fairy Tale 115
Asian Adventure.. 125
Paradise 131
Island of The Gods 133
Wedding Bells - November/December 2000... 149
October 2008... 171
Black Shadow 175
Lucky Girl 191
Mirror, Mirror, On The Wall 197
Cupid 205
    June 2010.. 234
    The Greatest Loss of All 240
Million Dollar Deal. 243
    April 2011. 243

PART 3 – Miracles Do Happen - Just Believe!

Miracles Do Happen, Just Believe! 267
There are no Treasures greater than Friends 269
Oh Please! Not Monsieur Cancer again?.. 279

In memory of my beautiful mum May –
I love you so much.

*Faith is the bird that feels the light and sings when
the dawn is still dark.*

Rabindranath Taqore (1861 – 1941)

Acknowledgements

To all those who have been with me, on my journey of empowerment, I would like to thank you from the bottom of my heart.

To my father Alexander, my dear Aunt Helen, and my good friend Edwina; thank you for supporting me through the years of strife and strain.

Thank you to the medical teams at: The Beatson Hospital, Oncology Centre; Maggie's Cancer Care Wellbeing Centre; Western Hospital, Oncology Unit, and Crosshouse Hospital, for all the medical care and emotional support they gave me.

Thank you to the people of Troon and my new found friends, Aida from Beach Cafe, David from Chit Chat Coffee Shop, Suzy from Yummy Things Coffee Shop and Cathy from Ivy Cottage.

To Diane and Claire from KKR Hair Salon, thank you for your advice and beauty tips when I had no hair.

Thank you to Gerry, Editor of *Word on the Street Magazine*.

I would also like to thank the Troon Writing Group, and give a special thank you to Jean Penman, for all the support given while I was writing the book.

Thank you to all at Troon Library and the staff of the Marr Educational Resource Centre, where I wrote my book, surrounded by the help, expertise, and kindness of all the staff.

Thank you to my Editor, Chris Bryce, Book Cover Graphic Artist, Alan Baird, and Interior Book Designer, Nigel Mitchell.

And, special thanks to my buddy, Meg, who collated the book with me by burning the midnight oil, and has been so wonderful in preparing my slides for the book's Self Help Presentations.

Author's Note

These events describe how I overcame adversity against all the odds. The scenarios described are factual.

Some names have been changed and various events slightly altered to protect the wellbeing of recognisable individuals.

In telling my story it is not my intention to demean any faith or culture, it is only, to tell the truth.

Rebellion is when you look a society in the face and say I understand who you want me to be, but now I am going to show you who I actually am.

Anthony Anaxagorou

To the women of Saudi Arabia and lands beyond; to those without a voice I say this:

"Let me be your voice, by my endeavour and pen; perhaps together we can be instrumental in creating much-needed legislation, protecting you and your rights, through truth and justice."

Find your Moral Compass

"We know in our heart of hearts what is right,

We can choose to ignore the feeling or act on it,

But, when we ignore it, we feel incomplete,

We know we have sold ourselves short,

It takes courage,

Sometimes great courage, but,

When we follow our conscience, we find real freedom."

PART 1

Top Gun

The Adventure Begins

November 1978, looking out of the aircraft window I catch my first glance of Saudi Arabia. It is 8 o'clock in the evening and darkness has fallen, but the city of Jeddah is well lit up with many sparkling lights. I can feel my heart beating with excitement as the aircraft touches down; what an adventure. Here I am, a Scottish lass, at the tender age of twenty, seeking adventure in a faraway land, where only Kings and men rule.

Would it be how I had imagined? A vast desert with oases and palm trees, made magical, like that of Aladdin, with flying carpets, beautiful white stallions with the magic of unicorns, and women dressed in silks, sitting in palaces, adorned with rubies and emeralds. Perhaps like Aladdin, I too would find a magic lamp?

Well, let's face it, at that age we like to believe that anything is possible!!!

As the doors of the aircraft open, one can feel the heat and sense the smells carried on the desert air.

From the minute I arrive at King Abdul Aziz Airport a totally new world awaits me and as I was soon to find out my destiny would be in a country of many parallels. The desert, arrayed in all her finery, oil wells, gold and diamond mines. The hospitality and kindness of the Bedouin, second to none, their camels and goats resting by their tents and, of course, for many, the obligatory four-wheel drive. Nearby, one may relax beside the cooling water of an oasis shaded by its palm trees, surrendering nourishing dates, ensuring the survival of its inhabitants.

The vibrant city with bright lights and tall glass towers, marble shopping malls with shops selling the latest couture from designers such as Chanel, Gucci and Dior, just to mention a few. Contrasted with a visit to the older part of the city, in downtown Jeddah, with the smell and aroma of freshly baked bread and Arabic coffee, made from a mixture of Arabic coffee beans, cardamom and colourful spices of saffron, cumin and dried lemons from around the Arabian Peninsula.

The old souq market is like an Aladdin's cave, with an abundance of gold and precious stones. Diamonds, sapphires, rubies, emeralds, and pearls straight from the oyster, on display. Most of the vendors, from Yemen, trading and selling their wares; astute businessmen with a great sense of pride.

My young eyes perceive the Saudi women as quite beautiful people, with their olive skin, thick black hair, and eyes like that of the gazelle. As I learn more about them, and their customs, many of the secrets of their stunning beauty, elegance, and finesse would come to light.

One of the most stylish shops, which I would frequent to buy my silk veils, encrusted with Swarovski diamonds, is called My Fair Lady. I always felt as if I was stepping into a small palace, with its crystal chandeliers and scents of musk and other rich perfumes wafting through the space. The women standing near small incense burners (mabkhara), filled with wood chips soaked in pure fragrant oils creating smoke that gently wafts through their silks and veils. The scents and perfumes known as 'oud' are so very beautiful and quite bewitching. If one were to receive 'oud' as a gift, then it would indeed be extravagance in a bottle.

In the street, I would arrange my veils to cover my body (habaya) and to cover my hair lightly (turha). It was not a must to cover one's face, although sometimes I did this for protection. As these beautiful, elegant Saudi women left the shop, to be driven off by a driver in either a Rolls Royce, Mercedes, or Lexus, I thought, how lucky are they!

However, as I was to find out shortly, and through personal experience, many of these women, as they get older or become ill, are replaced and become, like me, one of the untouchables.

I can honestly say at first I felt like a princess and very feminine in my silks. They were not at all the ugly designs that you see on the television, but the ones in 'my Arabia', flattering yet discreet. Through hard work, long hours and promotions I quickly climbed the ladder of success. It felt cool to be headhunted within the company, eventually becoming Top Gun and being the first woman in Saudi Arabian Airline history to join an all-male training team consisting of pilots, engineers and other male facilitators, conducting seminars throughout many continents. When I wasn't in the classroom, I might be jumping on and off an array of jets around the desert and throughout the world, as a Cabin Safety Inspector, staying at some of the most magnificent hotels, in stunning locations.

Throughout my career, I have been treated with so much respect, empathy and warmth from my peers. I can honestly say my chosen career path was never dull, and what an adventure.

Perhaps I did find that magic lamp after all.

On my first arrival at King Abdul Azziz Airport, I was met by a gentleman from Pakistan.

"Salam, Miss Lesley, welcome to Saudi Arabia and your cabin crew training. My name is Ahmed, from the Training Centre."

"Hello, Mr Ahmed," I replied.

"May I have your passport please, and I will guide you quickly through passport control and customs."

"Oh Yes, of course," I said, as I handed him my passport.

"Miss Lesley, inside this bag is a veil and coat to cover your hair and shoulders. You will see as you leave the airport all women wear the same. It is part of the Saudi culture. If you don't mind, can you please put it on before we leave the airport?"

"Of course," I said, rather bewildered at the apparel. It consisted of two parts: a black coat and a black scarf, both made from a polyester nylon mix and quite unbecoming. However, as I have already mentioned to you, I soon learned more about the beautiful silk veils worn by the majority of elegant Saudi women.

Mr Ahmed guided me to a waiting car.

"I will leave you now, Miss Lesley, and the driver, Mohammed, will take you to your residence which is downtown near the old souq."

"Thank you, Mr Ahmed".

"You have the day free tomorrow, Miss Lesley, and then on Saturday a driver will pick you up at your residence at 7.30 in the morning to bring you to the Training Centre. Have a lovely evening."

"Thank you, Mr Ahmed."

As I arrived at the complex, I was met by a lovely Turkish woman called Gul. "Hello," she said with a sweet smile.

"I work here in this building. I am known as a Resident Check Hostess and will look after you during your training."

I felt comfortable talking to Gul, already she was making me feel so at home.

"I have been a flight supervisor for many years, so if ever you are not sure about anything, please, just ask. Here is your welcome package for you to look through regarding some rules and regulations of the company. I have put some food in your apartment in case you are peckish. I know you will be tired Lesley but before I take you to your apartment let me introduce you to our Receptionists, Ali and Nasser, who will take good care of you."

There, sitting behind the reception desk were two of the kindest and funniest characters I would ever meet: Ali from Egypt, and wonderful Samir from Sudan. They, as it turned out, were not only receptionists but doubled up as international telephone operators and security guards. Many a night I would go down and sit with them at the reception, captivated by stories of their loved ones and lives back in their homelands.

The apartment complex where I was going to stay during training and for the next year was near the old city and airport. The fully furnished apartment, shared with other female cabin crew trainees, consisted of two doubles and one single bedroom, two bathrooms, and a kitchen living room/dining room. Our apartments would be cleaned daily by Sudanese men. This felt a bit awkward at the beginning, but we did get used to it. Although we did our own cooking, if ever we wanted a takeaway, then one would just call reception. Within thirty minutes a delicious shaurma with tehina (traditional bread wrap with spicy lamb or chicken) would be delivered to the apartment by one of the burly Sudanese, who were always so grateful for a wee tip (bakshish).

Gul and the other female supervisors, all of Arabic origin, dealt with any problems that might arise, making sure that when we went out, we had all returned by the curfew time of 1.00am in the morning.

No one was apparently allowed to stay out after curfew. In the future, I would find out that this was not necessarily true; an underworld existed, which I would one day be part of.

During training, one of the Instructors, Mr Khan, was very motivating and told us how he had started as a flight attendant, but his dream had always been to become an Instructor. That very day the seed for me was sown. In other words, my ambition became to achieve this also and do so very much more!

Every day, after classroom training, my friends and I would go over the road to a hotel called the Kandara, where we had permission to use the outdoor swimming pool. It was fabulous swimming in the pool and meeting up with lots of new friends. It was a mixed crowd. So many nationalities would gather there: Saudi, Lebanese, American, British, German and many more. Some were aviation crew members and pilots, others worked in the military, at the Embassy's, hospitals, and restaurants.

This was the Saudi Arabia you don't hear about or see on TV.

We could swim freely, wearing our bikinis, sip fresh fruit cocktails and have a great time. Our weekends were spent going on picnics at one of the private beaches. Embassy parties were frequent, where the finest of wines and cocktails were served. We would go out for dinner or visit the expatriates' compounds where there was always a party going on at the weekend, or we'd enjoy a scrumptious barbeque, watered down by a glass of wine, beer or home-made sediki (as refreshing as a gin & tonic, with a lemon slice).

In the seventies and eighties, it was quite a carefree life in Saudi Arabia. I only noticed laws becoming tighter after the first Gulf war of 1991.

I graduated in December 1978 and gained my wings as a Cabin Attendant. For the first month, I would be on standby for flights. It was so exciting, sitting with my suitcase ready, at the crew schedule, in the old airport, not knowing which destination I would be going to.

I remember the first night I was feeling a bit lonely and missing mum, thinking about her preparing for the Christmas festivities. An older

American pilot, waiting for his flight, started talking to me. I was so in awe of his stories as I listened to the countries and lands he had seen. Listening to him, I soon forgot my loneliness and smiled with contentment at things I was about to see and do.

The Flight schedulers were so kind; they would offer me wonderful flights. "Lesley, we are a crew member short for Paris, would you like to go?" Gosh, my eyes would light up "Yes please," and so I would be flying on one of the big jets for a five-day trip to Paris. This aircraft was highly technical at the time, with lifts on board to take you down to the hub of the aircraft where the galleys were. My salary was excellent, and in addition, we were paid expenses to cover our time in these amazing destinations.

This would only be the tip of the ice-berg!

Black Pearl

I have met a new friend, Anna. She had graduated in the class before me and what a wonderful friend she would become. She was a beautiful black girl from Eritrea in Ethiopia. Her mother being Ethiopian and her father, Italian. One day Anna told me all about her personal struggle to become an independent woman and feel empowered.

It was during the time when the Italians occupied Ethiopia that her mum and dad met each other, fell in love and before long were married. Her mum was a black beauty with skin like silk and customary tribal markings on her face, which must have been quite a painful ritual for any young woman to have to pass through. These women, of such beauty and strength, were known by the Italians as the "Black Pearls."

Although Anna's mum was Muslim, she was to follow her father's religion and go to Catholic school. While still a little girl her father sadly passed away and the young family were destitute and in despair. The political and economic situation was not so great in Eritrea at that time. Anna's mum had no money, with no prospects. So, she decided to travel to Saudi Arabia with her two little children, Anna and her brother, hoping to carve a better life for themselves in this oil-rich state.

A few months later, the family, with little belongings, made their way to Saudi Arabia, where Anna's mum was employed as a maid in the house of a wealthy family; the master of the house being both rich and well connected. This was during the 1960's, and Anna was leading a very happy and contented life as the master and mistress of the household were both good and kind to the little family. Anna and her brother were sent to Muslim school (Islam being the only religion recognised and practised in the country.) At school, Anna excelled, forging ahead in her studies, speaking fluent Arabic, English and Italian, as well as her native Amharic language. Two little princesses attending the same school, realising Anna's potential, asked her to please help them with their homework. Anna agreed and was paid in kind with a daily selection of chocolate bars and candy; every little girl's dream. I suppose one would call it a win–win situation for both herself and the princesses. Anna grew up to be a beautiful and intelligent young woman, but she wanted more out of life than the majority of women living in Saudi Arabia had at that time.

Whether from a rich Saudi family or not, women are usually married off at a young age and have started a family. A woman having a career was very rarely on the agenda of any family. Even now, to this day, it is taboo for Saudi woman to work in the aviation sector or any similar field. It's incredible that to this day they cannot travel anywhere without the permission of a male family member. Can you imagine not being able to travel anywhere without your father, brother or husband's permission? Do many of the Saudi men make good husbands, by western standards, you might ask? Of course, there are some, but in my twenty-two years of living and working amongst the people I met very few. I can tell you that adultery is rampant, like a plague, which unfortunately I would experience in my own marriage. I can tell you solemnly, there is no freedom for the Saudi women, Royal or not. Have you ever heard of a Saudi Queen? Of course not, it is the land of men, ruled by a King.

Young Anna did not want to go down the path of being married to someone she did not know, and perhaps did not like. One day she had a conversation with her mother that would change her life. She had told her mother that she did not want to become a maid, like her mother, nor be married. Her mother explained that there are no real jobs for women in Saudi Arabia and marriage was the only option.

Anna had seen the aeroplanes flying over, and dreamt of travelling to faraway lands. She wanted to be like one of the beautiful women she had seen at the airport, dressed so femininely and smart.

Her mother tried to explain the reason her daughter could not become a Flight Attendant. It was heartbreaking for her mother to explain the reason was, although Anna was a beautiful woman, there was no openings for black women in this type of career. Anna's smile soon disappeared and was replaced by tears. She pleaded with her mother to talk to the master, to see if he could help. Sure enough that same night, Anna's mum told the master of the house about Anna's hopes and dreams. To her surprise, the master listened intently and said he would talk to the President of the airline, who was his friend. The master kept his word and above everyone's expectations Anna became a flight attendant. History in the making, the first black woman in Saudi Airlines. After hearing her story, I arranged to meet her mum.

"Lesley, my mum is coming over tonight to meet you and cook you some nice dinner."

"Oh, fantastic Anna. I am looking forward to meeting her."

That evening we had a feast. Anna's mum arrived wearing traditional Ethiopian dress called Habesha Kemis, made from a beautiful cloth called Shemma. She spoke little English, but what a beautiful smile. We chatted and laughed till midnight, Anna translating for her mum whenever needed. Her mum's laugh was infectious; such a big heart, what a beautiful woman. We all retired to bed with full bellies and very content.

It was about five o'clock in the morning, just before sunrise, when I was woken by a faint noise coming from the living room. I slowly made my way from the bedroom through the darkness of the hallway to where the sound was coming. It was quite scary. Was someone in the apartment? Quietly popping my head round, the door, I could just make out the silhouette of a woman kneeling on a prayer mat (musallah) and softly reciting Arabic words. I still couldn't see her face as her back was to me, but as she stood up, she turned round with the greeting "Salaam Alaykum" (peace be to you). I smiled, to my relief, it was Anna's mum. She gently smiled back then knelt back down to continue her prayers. The call for worshippers to come to prayer echoed through the darkness from the nearby minarets; I always remember thinking how serene and beautiful everything seemed as the sun was about to rise.

A couple of years passed and Anna eventually would choose to live in one of our overseas bases in Thailand, where she would fall in love, and marry a handsome and kind Thai gentlemen called Paisarn. I was honoured to be her bridesmaid. I flew to Bangkok for her wedding. Anna was stunning in her dress of Thai silk and lace. My dress was a rose coloured Thai silk gown with matching pink flowers in my hair. There were two ceremonies, a morning Christian ceremony held in a Catholic church and in the evening a Buddhist ceremony held in one of the temples. Both ceremonies were beautiful, pious, and full of love.

The following year Anna was expecting her first child, and as there was no maternity leave at that time within the company, she had no choice but to resign. She had had a wonderful career, being promoted to an In-flight supervisor, found a good husband and was ecstatic as she was fulfilling her dreams of now having her own family and embarking on another journey. On one of her final flights she had an encounter from the past. As the seat belt sign came on for landing one of the passengers in first class was still standing. Anna asked the lady politely to take her seat. As Anna walked to the first class galley, the passenger followed her. Anna turned as the lady tapped her on the shoulder.

The lady lifted her veil (necab) and said, "Hello Anna, don't you remember me?" Anna smiled she recognised her VIP passenger and they hugged each other. It was the little princess from school now all grown up.

I often think of Anna and what a great example of cross culture, as she was born a Christian, studied Islam, and eventually married a Buddhist. Definitely, there would be no apartheid for Anna.

One can never consent to creep when one feels an impulse to soar.
(Helen Keller – 1880 - 1968)

Live simply with no barriers; we are one, it is called the human race.
(Lesley A Sehli – 1958 -   )

The King and I

Time passes and I really enjoying flying, seeing so many different countries. On one day I caught up with my lovely check hostess Gul.

"I am going to London next week Lesley," she said, "I have left a deposit for a beautiful mink coat in Harrods, I am so looking forward to going back to collect it."

"Wow, it sounds lovely Gul."

"By the way Lesley, you have been requested to operate a VIP flight."

"What do you mean?" I asked her, "I don't fly on VIP flights. I have heard a lot of stories about the girls who fly VIP. They say that some of the passengers on these private flights expect more from a female flight attendant than just operating a flight?"

"Oh no Lesley," she said, "That is not true. Yes there are some girls like that, just as there are anywhere in the world, but the majority are just like you they are there purely for the safety of the passengers."

"But these other girls Gul, who are they?" I asked rather innocently.

"Well Lesley, some of them are girlfriends of the princes and other royals. They don't actually fly, or at least not very much."

I wasn't too convinced by what Gul was saying about these other girls but I was going to give her the benefit of the doubt at this point. I was suspicious that there was some kind of racket going on. During my career, my paths with these girls would cross, but I will tell you something, we should never assume!

The total history of almost anyone would shock almost everyone.
Mignon Mclaughlin (1913 – 1983)

The next day I went along to the VIP offices and there I was met by a Lebanese supervisor called Rony. I have to say that I didn't feel very comfortable in her presence, perhaps due to the fact that she wasn't very friendly or perhaps it was the rumours that I heard about her, suggesting she was a mamasan for the Saudi royals and rich business men. Minutes later a black Saudi man entered her office.

"This is Mr Yaser, Manager of the VIP Section."

I knew exactly who he was. I am sitting with the big kahuna, the royals' personal papasan. Sorry to say he had no positive attributes. His face had so many lumps and bumps, like planet Krypton, and my goodness was he loud. Between the two of them I felt I was in the lion's lair, a den of iniquity. I just wanted to get out of that office.

"Tomorrow Lesley we would like you to fly on a Royal domestic flight to the capital Riyadh," said Yaser.

"But I don't fly on VIP flights; I have my own scheduled flight tomorrow."

Abruptly Yaser interrupted,

"Every new flight attendant gets the chance to fly one VIP flight and you have already been removed from your scheduled flight. It is supposed to be an honour to be chosen on such a flight."

This guy makes my skin crawl and I feel so intimidated by him.

"Make sure you are on time tomorrow at the airport for the flight."

"Who is the VIP?" I ask.

"You will know tomorrow," said Yaser.

Nervously I said "Okay," I just wanted to get out of their office.

That night I hardly slept. Why did I agree to go on this flight? My imagination started to work overtime. Oh stop, I told myself, it will probably be fine, but if anyone tries to act smart, I will certainly be telling them where to go, regardless of their ancestry!

The next day I met with the regular VIP crews, and although most were friendly I did feel like a fish out of water. The VIP boss Yaser was on board but for some reason, I just wanted to keep a distance from him. I felt there was something just not quite right. He had positioned me at the rear of the aircraft, with the security, and just as the announcement was made that the VIP's were boarding, one of the regular crews, a beautiful friendly English girl called Janet, informed me that the VIP was HRH Crown Prince Fahad, the future king. The short flight went smoothly and then just as the seat belt sign came on for landing, one of the male Saudi crew members told me that Yaser wanted to see me at the front cabin.

"Why?" I asked nervously.

"I don't know," he grunted, "just go the front."

Nervously, I went to see Yaser who was holding a magnificent bottle of perfume in his hand.

"Lesley I want you to take this perfume to the Crown Prince. Don't worry, I will be with you."

As we entered the private lounge of HRH Crown Prince Fahad, Yaser introduced me.

"Your Excellency, this is Miss Lesley."

Crown Prince Fahad smiled and greeted me in English.

"Lovely to meet you, Miss Lesley."

I have to say I immediately felt at ease; his demeanour was like that of a father.

"Are you travelling with us tomorrow Miss Lesley?"

"Where are you going?" I surprisedly blurted out, forgetting, for a moment in time, that this man was the future King. I felt my face flush with embarrassment.

"Well Miss Lesley," he said reassuringly, "we are going, Inshalla (God Willing), to my summer palace in Tangiers, and you would be most welcome."

I tried to contain my excitement about what was happening, and softly answered,

"It would be an honour, your Majesty."

He then held out his ghutrah (male headscarf) on which I was to spray the perfume, under the direction of Yaser.

"Thank you," he smiled.

He looked to Yaser,

"Miss Lesley will be with us tomorrow."

"Of course, your Excellency," Yaser replied.

The Crown Prince turned gently saying,

"Then I will see you, 'Inshalla', tomorrow Miss Lesley, Ma Salaama (Goodbye)."

"Ma Salaama, your Majesty."

The next day seemed surreal; I was feeling so excited at the prospect of travelling with the crown prince, who in the near future would be crowned King Fahad Abdul Aziz of Saudi Arabia.

It's a lovely summers day; I can feel the softness of the desert breeze on my face as I board the Royal Aircraft, aptly named, HM1. A magnificently designed, specially adapted 747 jumbo jet with its own operating theatre and doctor on board. The interior was like that of a small palace. Throughout the aircraft there are numerous lounges, the walls are decorated with breathtaking abstract murals depicting many aspects of the Saudi life: the desert with all her finery, the riches of the gold mines, the cooling oasis and strength of the falcon all edged in gold. Silk carpets are laid throughout the aisles, Persian rugs of all colours, so soft to the touch. Every seatbelt is gold. Individual lounges with en suite bedrooms for the royal family and every type of amenity one could imagine. The aircraft is busy, with dignitaries, staff and members of the Royal household occupied on final preparations for the Kings arrival.

Security personnel stand by, some dressed in smartly tailored suits, others ornately, as though they had stepped back in time to that of Lawrence of Arabia, in their traditional Saudi dress with a gold bejewelled dagger proudly and prominently worn.

Gourmet chefs with their teams are busily preparing the kitchens, indeed, food fit for a king. Hors d'oeuvres of caviar, prawns, salmon and Arabian mezza (tapas). Fridges of succulent lobsters, king prawns, chateaubriand and fillet steak, that melts in one's mouth like butter. The cheeses and fruits are from all around the world, the desserts have a Harrods label, probably flown from London during the night.

The household maids and nannies are making themselves comfortable, carefully securing the Gucci and Dior luggage of the Royals.

A cascade of cars has arrived; the Crown Prince is here! As members of the royal family board the aircraft, there is such a feeling of pride and anticipation amongst everyone waiting.

"Salaam Alaykum," (greetings to all) the future King says, with such a warm smile, as he enters the doorway and is led to his private quarters.

It's a wonderful flight. After lunch, everyone is relaxing. Some of the younger princes are playing cards with solid gold coins, as I have a chat with the Crown Prince.

"I am so happy, Lesley, that you decided to travel with us. Tomorrow evening, you and the crew are all invited for dinner at my summer palace."

"Thank you so much, your Majesty."

"Now tell me more about Scotland Lesley. Are the people as pretty and polite like you?"

"Yes your Majesty, they are indeed a very kind and hospitable people, just like the hospitality of your Kingdom."

"What is the climate like Lesley? I hear it is rather cold."

"Well, actually, we have four seasons which is the reason why we have such breathtaking scenery, lochs, beaches, forests and woodlands, where the deer roam freely under a blanket of magnificent purple heather."

"Perhaps I will visit one day," said the Prince, as he calls his aide, Ali, to bring us some mint tea.

On arrival to Tangiers, cars take us to our residence where I and other members of the entourage would stay for the next few days. We are all handed, by one of the king's staff, individual envelopes each containing $2000 to spend that day. How wonderful, how lucky don't you think?!

After spending the afternoon relaxing and being pampered in the hotel spa, I get ready for dinner at the palace. I feel quite pretty having chosen to wear a cream silk Dior dress and sparkling Gucci sandals that I had recently bought.

On arrival at the Prince's magnificent summer palace, we are met by one of the household who ushers us through to the most amazing Banquet area. We see marble floors and columns, silk rugs, chandeliers sparkling like diamonds in the candlelight while a quartet play soft melodies in the background. Waiters in tuxedos welcome us with a choice of cocktails as more guests arrive. Everyone stands up as Crown Prince Fahad enters the room, greeting everyone as we follow him through to dinner. One of the ushers approaches me:

"Miss Lesley, Prince Fahad has asked that you kindly join him at his table."

Wow! what a privilege A moment in history for me.

Seated beside the Crown Prince, I was so in awe, as he greeted me with an outstretched hand.

"Salaam Alaykum Lesley, thank you for joining me, lovely Scottish lady."

"Alaykum Salaam, your Highness" (and greetings to you.)

We conversed and laughed through the evening, while the waiters looked after our every whim. The table was a sumptuous banquet like Scheherazade and a thousand and one nights. Huge candelabras, fresh scented floral displays, crystal glasses that sparkled in tune with the chandeliers. Platters of seafood, succulent whole lambs which have been slowly roasted with many spices. Fruits from around the globe prepared and beautifully presented by master chefs, varieties of decadent deserts of chocolate, cream and passion fruits. After the banquet Crown Prince Fahad stood up and said:

"I would like all of you here today to accompany me now to the Regal room; I have something to give you before our fond farewell."

We politely followed his majesty to a magnificent room of palatial decoration with designs of red velvet and gold. Prince Fahad opened his arms, thanking us all for being his guests, while pointing to a magnificent gold embellished table in front of him. A pyramid of one hundred blue velvet boxes awaited us, carefully arranged like the advert for Ferrero Rocher. Prince Fahad asked everyone to come forward and take a box and while looking at me, he said

"This box is for you Miss Lesley."

As I glanced round the room, everyone was opening their boxes with smiles of wonderment. The Crown Prince handed me the last box, which I carefully opened and just like Scheherazade my eyes opened with delight at my gifts of Chopard, a diamond bevelled watch, a necklace, its pendant a basket of flowers in diamonds, and a ring with diamonds like icebergs. Quite overwhelmed, I thanked his Majesty for his kindness. As Prince Fahad said his good byes, I left to go back to my residence. What an enchanting end to a most magical evening!

Next day over breakfast Yaser informed all the crew that we had been cordially invited to the palace for a barbecue by the swimming pool. What a lovely afternoon we had. The Crown Prince joined us for a while joining in the laughter and happy atmosphere.

"I am going to my private yacht in Marbella tomorrow for a couple of days. Would you like to join us, Miss Lesley?"

"Thank you, Excellency, but tomorrow I am flying back to Jeddah as it's my summer vacation. I am going home to Scotland, but thank you," I said, rather perturbed.

"That's fine Lesley, I hope we will meet again, goodnight," he said, as he stood up and retired back into the main palace.

As the sun set I was quite happy knowing that this would be my last night in Morocco, I had a feeling it was time to bail out.

Murder Most Foul

Arriving back in Jeddah I tried calling Gul to share all my news. There was no answer. A day passed and still no sign of my supervisor. Perhaps she is already in London collecting her new mink coat? The following day I met up with lovely Samir on the reception desk.

"Salaam Samir, I have been calling Gul and still no answer. Do you know where she is?"

"Haven't you heard Lesley?"

"Heard what?" I asked him.

"I am sorry to tell you Lesley, Gul went out the other night with some Saudi friends and never returned back home."

"What do you mean, Samir, she didn't return back home?"

"They found her body, full of drugs, dumped at the roadside."

"What!" I said in disbelief. "Who would do such a thing?"

"We don't know Lesley. The police were called, everyone's talking, we all believe it's murder?"

I was numb!!!!

"But Samir, everyone loved her. She was so kind to us, all of us."

"I know Lesley, but she mingled with too many of the high and mighty. Perhaps she upset one of them, and we believe she just knew too much?"

The questions we had about our lovely supervisor Gul were never answered. We were told absolutely nothing. It was all kept under wraps but one sure thing, Gul would never wear her beautiful mink coat!

Unbeknown to me at this point in time, in the near future, I would be offered the same position as Gul had been working in and my eyes would definitely be opened.

1980-1985
Exciting Times

First Placement – based in Thailand

I have made brilliant friends here in Thailand and honestly I feel like I have won the lottery. I have a Thai maid called Natcha, an older lady, who cleans the house and cooks scrummy Thai cuisine for me. She is quiet and soft spoken and caring as many of the Thai's are. One can only respect and admire such a people.

Second Placement – based in Philippines

I am staying in a beautiful condominium on the famous Roxas Boulevard with breathtaking views of Manila Bay. The Filipinos are a very cultured and hospitable people. Many are of mixed-race, their roots are of Chinese or Spanish origin, called mestizo (male) or mestiza (female). A colourful people, who work hard and play hard, music being in their blood. There are many very wealthy Filipinos but alas so many are living in dire poverty.

Child – Mestizo

Tonight I am looking forward to catching up with my colleague and good friend Alyssa for a girlie night.

Alyssa said, "Tonight shall we visit one of the traditional native Filipino restaurants where the chef's sing as they cook in front of us."

"Wow, Alyssa, sounds cool!"

What a night it was, just as she had described. Ordering numerous scrumptious dishes, accompanied by the wonderful voices of the Chefs, comparable to that of Placido Domingo.

"Oh Alyssa, we have ordered too much food. This beautiful Chateaubriand, what shall we do with it?"

"We can ask them to wrap it and take it home."

As we left the restaurant, a small boy was standing. He must have been about four years old. "Going by his looks, he is one of the street children," said Alyssa. "His father might be an American soldier who had been stationed here. Sadly, there a lot of cases like this here in Manila. The poor little things are abandoned by both parents and left to fend for themselves."

Poor little Mestizo, I thought.

"Mabuhay," (hello in Tagalog) I said to the little boy.

My heart melted at the vision in front of me; a grubby wee face, piercing blue eyes, sandy coloured hair, wearing only shorts and barefoot. He smiled and gestured with his hand at his mouth.

"He is telling you he is hungry Lesley."

"Okay little man, here are some pesos."

As I gave him the pesos, into his tiny hand, he pointed to the foil.

"Gosh Alyssa, I think he wants the meat. I am going to give it to him".

As I handed him the meat, what a smile appeared on that wee boy's face. With heavy hearts we turned to walk the other way, but little Mestizo tugged at my skirt. As I turned to look at him, he held out the pesos.

"What is he doing Alyssa? What does he want?"

"He doesn't want anything Lesley, he only wants to return the pesos to you, to pay for the meat in the foil."

"Oh dear, how cruel the world can be Alyssa."

I knelt beside him, trying hard to hold back my tears. "Oh no little boy, these pesos are for you, everything is for you."

His little face lit up. He turned and disappeared round the corner.

"Let's follow him Alyssa and see where he goes."

No sooner had we gone around the corner than we saw our little Mestizo sit on the side of the road and begin to whistle. Out of nowhere about twenty little street children suddenly appear. They joined our little Mestizo, as he opened the foil, and all those beautiful, grubby, little faces lit up with glee as tonight they would tuck into a feast!

Why for some does it have to be this way? The haves and the have not's?

(No snowflake in an avalanche ever feels responsible)
Voltaire (1694 – 1778)

Rock a bye baby

It is a night flight from Jeddah to Manila, about twelve hours flying time, mostly over water.

About six hours into the flight, the lights are low, some passengers are watching movies, while others snuggle under their blankets.

A passenger approaches me from the Economy Class:

"Where are the toilets?" she asks.

"I am sorry, Madam, this is first class."

"Oh please," she says "I don't feel very well."

I helped her through the first class cabin to where the lavatories were.

"Thank you," she said.

Ten minutes passed, with still no sign of her. She didn't come back out of the toilet.

"Are you okay, Madam?"

There was no answer.

I knocked the door, again asking

"Are you okay, Madam?"

Again nothing, I slowly opened the door and to my horror I found the woman slumped on the floor.

"What's happening Madam, are you sick?"

Nervously she said, "I think I am going to have my baby, my waters have just broken."

"What now?" I responded (I know stupid question).

I pressed the lavatory emergency call button and within seconds one of the crew arrived to help.

"We will assist you upstairs Madam; we have some comfortable sofas that you can relax on."

We made an announcement for a doctor, and I informed the captain, who I have flown with many times. The other flight attendant whispers in my ear,

"There is no doctor on board Lesley."

"Okay, we will deal with it. Get the first aid kit and stay beside her. Where is a doctor when you need one?"

"Captain, one of our Filipino passengers is in labour. Her waters have broken. I think birth is imminent. We have announced for a doctor, but unfortunately, there is none on board.

"You will have to manage it Lesley. I am sure you will be fine. Good Luck, and let me know as soon as she has delivered."

"Yes sir," I replied, leaving the cockpit, as my adrenalin and training started to kick in.

"What is your name, Madam?" I asked her.

"Tess she replied, its short for Theresa after one of the patron saints."

"Oh what a beautiful name," I replied.

"Tess, my name is Lesley and this is Angie, we still have some time to land but the captain has radioed to Singapore and they are waiting for our arrival. Please don't worry, you are in good hands, we are trained to help you and will stay by your side."

Angie prepared one of the baby cradles, with soft pillows and blankets, waiting for the wee arrival.

I couldn't believe it, a Jumbo jet and not one doctor or nurse on board. Well, let me take that back, there was one nurse. Can you believe it? Tess!

I guided the baby's head. "Another wee push Tess. Oh, here he is. You have a have a beautiful wee boy. Well done!"

We tied the cord and laid the most beautiful and handsome wee bundle beside his mum. Tess had been wonderful, as well as delivering, can you believe it, she still had time to talk us through what was happening. Relieved, I informed the captain of the precious bundle and that mum and baby were both doing well. Just after landing in Singapore the captain made an announcement to the passengers:

"Ladies and gentlemen, I have a happy announcement to make, we departed with three hundred passengers, and we have landed with three hundred and one."

To which there was a loud applause heard throughout the aircraft.

Third Placement – Based in Frankfurt
Mayday! Mayday!

I have now been promoted to Second in Command of Cabin. Today I am operating a flight from Jeddah back to Frankfurt. The weather forecast is quite bad and the captain has mentioned that there is a heavy snowfall in Europe, therefore we might hit some turbulence en route. I have a very professional crew. It is a full load flight and one of the Saudi first class passengers is travelling to Europe for heart surgery. He has his own oxygen cylinder and is accompanied by his son. Even so, I have asked that the ground staff seat him not far from my jump seat so I can keep an eye on him.

About four hours into the flight the captain calls me to the cockpit.

"Lesley, we are going into bad weather; it will be a bit of a bumpy ride. We just cannot clear this snow storm. We have to divert to Paris. There is too much snow in Frankfurt and visibility is bad. Please inform the passengers and get everyone into their seats."

"Yes Sir," I said, as I left the cockpit.

No sooner had I made an announcement to the passengers, then the aircraft started to shake as it hit the turbulence. Gosh! That was a big drop. I have never known such turbulence; the aircraft was being shaken like a rag doll. I hope it stops soon, my passenger with the heart problem isn't looking so good. I sensed something wasn't quite right and felt there was more going on than just the turbulence. We should be landing, but instead we have been holding a circling pattern for the last thirty minutes. I went to the cockpit, holding onto whatever was available to keep my feet firmly on the ground. In the cockpit so much is going on, bells ringing and dials spinning, the pilots look as though they have a crisis on their hands. I waited; the captain turned.

"Lesley, we are having a problem with the hydraulics and the landing gear is not coming down. We will not be able to circle much longer as we are running low in fuel; however, even though we have poor visibility and the weather has worsened, we have no choice but to make an emergency landing."

"Right Sir, shall I tell the passengers?"

"No Lesley, we don't want panic. The scenario is that we are going to try and bring the gears down manually. However, we could also have a problem with the breaking system after we land. So young lady, prepare your cabin crew, ensure all doors are in evacuation mode and that all the passengers are secured in their seats. You have thirty minutes till approach."

"Okay Captain."

As I left the cockpit, I turned back to the pilots knowing that our lives were in their hands. I know each one of them, they are all professional at their job. I know they will get us down safe! Doors were prepared, passengers secured in their seats, babies removed from their bassinets. I briefed the flight attendants,

"It will probably be a bumpy landing. Stay in your seats until we completely stop. Good Luck everyone."

The crew took it all in their stride, calmly and discreetly they carried out their duties to prepare their areas for an emergency landing. I called the cockpit

"Cabin is secure Captain. We are ready."

"Okay Lesley, the tower has cleared us for landing, we are on our final approach."

"Thank you, Captain. Good luck, Sir,"

I looked at my sick passenger. I thought, he knows something is happening and smiled to him.

28

"Don't worry," I whispered gently "we will be all right; we will be landing soon."

He smiled back "Shukran" (Thank you).

I can hear my own heart beating. Please God let the gears come down! Suddenly, I heard a loud thud. What was that? A second thud. What is happening? Seconds later, thank goodness, I think I have just heard the undercarriage and wheels going down. We are landing at such a speed on the runway, will we ever slow down? We are gaining such momentum, bypassing all the fire trucks. We are going to run out of runway soon! The pilots are trying to break; what a noise. God! Please help us to stop, I prayed. One of the passengers is screaming in the back, my eyes are fixed on the emergency handle. Only seconds from disaster, the aircraft suddenly starts to slow down and, to our relief, stops dead at the end of the runway. There is only silence in the cabin as the fire trucks move in. We are okay, we have made it. We open the doors to loud applause from our passengers.

My special passenger with the heart problem smiles, "Well done, thank you," he said, "that was the biggest thrill I have had, in a long time."

As the final passengers leave the aircraft my crew and I are so relieved and yet aware how the scenario could have played out so differently. Tonight we will celebrate in the beautiful Meridian Hotel in Paris. Lots of champagne on ice. Just another day at the office!

1985-1996
Women Power in the Desert!

Well, I am now saying goodbye to Frankfurt as I have decided to return to mother base, Saudi Arabia. I must keep my eye on the ball, so as to move up the ladder of success and attain every promotion I possibly can. My position back in Saudi will be a management position. My piggy bank is getting fatter.

It's great being back in Jeddah, six months has already passed. How time flies when one is enjoying oneself. Nasser, from the higher management, wants to see me in his office tomorrow. I have no idea why, but I know he is one of the good guys, a gentleman. In fact, he was the one who interviewed me in London and gave me the opportunity to have this wonderful career. I am so looking forward to catching up with him.

"Good Morning, Lesley, how are you?"

"Good morning, Mr Nasser, it is so lovely to meet you once again."

"Are you enjoying your work in our company Lesley?"

"Oh, yes Sir, very much and no day is ever the same."

"I am pleased to hear from your superiors that you are indeed excelling in your work and it is for this reason that I have called you here to my office. I want you to go on a Safety Inspector course and when qualified you will operate the desert flights, safety checking the cabin crew. It's a great step in promotion Lesley, what do you think?"

"Yes Sir, it would be a great opportunity. I didn't realise, Mr Nasser, that women could hold such a position. I thought such a promotion was only open to Saudi male crew."

"That is true Lesley, this is a trial for Saudi Arabian Airlines. There has never been a woman in this position, let alone a foreigner. With the experience you already have, we are sure that you will be very successful in this role, working with our male ground personnel and also with our passengers, the majority who trace back to the historic Bedouin tribes."

"Well Sir, any time I have flown to these desert stations I have found the Bedouins to be none other than salt of the earth. It is the first class city dwellers that can sometimes be bit of a handful." We laughed.

"I know what you mean Lesley. There are three females whom we have chosen for the course."

"How many students will there be in total?"

"There will be a total of twenty students; the other seventeen will be Saudi males. The class will be starting next week. It is an intensive five-day course. I have full confidence in you Lesley, making the grade. Please make me proud."

My face lit up. "Oh thank you Mr Nasser, I will not let you down."

"I know," he said.

On leaving his office I gleefully smiled as I murmured under my breath "Yes! I have done it, my first big promotion."

The training was an intensive five days of theory, practicals and written exams. We certainly burned the midnight oil. And guess what? We made history, all three girls got through. Amongst hundreds of crew we are the first women to achieve this honour. WHOPPEE! I know I am bragging but I feel brilliant! Woman power in Saudi Arabia, it can be done!

Life is either a daring adventure or nothing at all.
Helen Keller

I think this was one of my happiest times in my career. The Bedouins were a joy, some of the kindest people I would ever meet. The women hugging me as they entered through the door with their children, so excited about the prospect of their wee adventure on an airplane. The teenage girls with their hair adorned with sweet jasmine flowers and velvet black khol accentuating the beauty of their eyes. Some betrothed and in bridal gown going to meet their chosen husbands for the first time, henna painted delicately on their hands, emphasising an imminent celebration. The scent of sweet musk fills the cabin.

On a first class seat, a very grand hooded falcon, the prince of birds, proudly sits, very strong, very still, very alert, listening to the voice of his master; waiting for his every command. Whether travelling North to the city of Abha with its cool climate and valley of trees, where its local inhabitants of mischievous baboons reside, or to Gizan, with its hot, dry desert landscape, where the awe inspiringly beautiful desert rose flourishes. The Holy City of Medina, cradling in her arms Mecca, the sanctuary of Islam, where during Haj pilgrims from all over the world flock. Some so very old and aware that this will probably be their last time to visit this holy shrine, many of them having saved all their life to make this remarkable trip. Old couples from as far afield as Indonesia and beyond, boarding the flight to the holy city, with copper kettles full of sweet mint tea which they offer to you in small cups as they make themselves comfortable on their seats for the short desert hop. One can only admire such passion, kindness, devotion and dedication. Humanity at its best!

During the Eid celebration the station manager in Medina always spoils us during our ground stop, his nickname is Mr Ramadan.

"Salaam, Miss Lesley, my wife has prepared dinner for the crew."

"Oh Shukran, Mr Ramadan, we are famished."

Folding down the seat backs in first class we prepare the area for a sumptuous Saudi feast. Succulent lambs, prepared in many spices, lying on a bed of rice. Followed by dessert, can you believe it, in the middle of the desert, homemade cooling pistachio ice cream. The Bedouin is kindness in abundance. This is my Arabia!

Underworld

I am really enjoying these last few months in my new position as a Safety Inspector. Today I received a call, yet again, from the manager's office.

"Miss Lesley, Mr Nasser wants you to report to his office tomorrow morning, first thing."

"Can you tell me why?" I asked.

"No sorry, just be here around nine o'clock."

The rest of the day I worried over what the urgency was. Why did he want to see me in his office? Did I make a mistake while conducting one of the safety checks? I was absolutely clueless, anyway, I will put it on the back burner as tonight I am going to my friend Julie and her husband's house for dinner and a relaxing glass of bubbly.

Next day, I met Nasser at his office.

"Good morning Lesley, I am hearing nothing but glowing reports from everyone who has been working with you in your new position. I knew in London when I recruited you, it was the right decision."

"Thank you, Sir."

"Are you enjoying your new position?"

"Absolutely Sir."

"Well, I have another position to offer you, it is actually a promotion to an even higher management level. You will still be a Safety Inspector, but this added position is on ground, very sensitive and rather delicate, if you agree to accept it. I believe you can manage it. If you agree your ground title will be Resident Check hostess and you will be the first British woman and the youngest to hold such a position. How old are you actually Lesley?"

"I am twenty-six years old, Sir."

"My goodness Lesley, you are still so very young, but already you have

35

proven yourself to us. We have chosen you because of your work ethic; you are clever, honest, strong and people trust you, they know they can rely on you Lesley. What do you think regarding this position?"

"Well Mr Nasser, I am indeed honoured. What will my job entail?"

"You will handle the crews that live on the compound, ensuring everyone returns safe from flights or social activities by midnight, curfew time. Tomorrow you will meet the other members of the team. Your new manager is called Miss Gabrielle, from Lebanon. However, I will always be here, Lesley, if at any time you need a chat."

"Okay, thank you, Mr Nasser. I will give it a go."

"Great, Lesley, I will inform Gabrielle to expect to see you tomorrow morning, in her office, for a briefing around 10.00 a.m."

Leaving Mr Nasser's office, I was excited about this new promotion when suddenly my thoughts went back to Gul. This was the position she held all those years ago, before she was found dead under suspicious circumstances. I wonder exactly what my role will be? I have a feeling Mr Nasser hasn't told me everything. Never mind, tomorrow I will meet the team and hopefully find out what I have let myself in for.

Human Rights Violations against Women!

A few months have passed and I am settling into my new position as ground management. I have completed some counselling and psychology courses and have learned lots of new procedures. To my surprise, I really do enjoy the work. I am the youngest member of the team. The others are mainly of Arabic origin, hailing from countries such as Lebanon, Syria, Palestine and Tunisia. I have learned a lot from my manager Gabrielle. I feel I have developed into quite a strong character, and I definitely do stick up for the underdog. There is no sitting on the fence for me. In the compound there can be anything up to 1,000 women residing at any one time. If any of the women return home to the compound late, after curfew time and a wee bit worse for wear, probably having drunk a bit too much bubbly, I don't report them. My main concern is that they have returned back home safe. I am just happy that they have had a pleasant evening and were able to relax.

We all know, both Saudi and foreigner alike, the rules of the kingdom regarding alcohol, parties and dating. Hypocrisy is the name of the game, to which I myself am witness. I know for a fact that as with so many of the draconian rules of this country it is the Saudi's themselves, the so called elite, who break their own laws. They hold many of the parties in their palaces, mansions and homes, alcohol runs like the river Nile, and they dance all night to the latest sounds. So, who are the ones who make life for so many unbearable in Saudi Arabia?

They are called Muttawa (religious police). Quite often you will see them walking in the marketplace, carrying a stick, which they are not slow to use on passers-by, if they feel that the person is not behaving piously enough in their eyes. They are usually accompanied by the regular police for protection as they are so disliked by the majority of the Saudi society. One could say they suffer terribly from distorted vision as to what is right and what is wrong and hence one feels that they will never understand the true meaning of humanity. Their human rights violations against women include inhumane whippings, stonings, other means of execution, and this is along with injustice to society as a whole. Both Saudis and foreigners know the risks of a pleasant night leading to beatings and imprisonment, if discovered by Muttawa.

I remember one evening, shopping in the souq, wearing my veils, fully covered except for my face. I was in a beautiful shopping mall admiring a pool with giant turtles swimming gracefully around. Suddenly I heard a screech like a banshee, I turned to find one of these Muttawas with his stick raised shouting at me!

"Cover your face infidel, cover your face or you won't go to heaven."

Though shocked by such an outburst, I was still able to compose myself and looking him straight in the eye I said:

"I don't want to go to heaven if it is full of merciless people like you."

I continued to walk on knowing that this time I was lucky to escape his wrath. Unfortunately, if I had been a Saudi woman I would probably have felt his anger; beaten by his stick and taken to prison to languish for such a stance. What injustice and human right violators they are. They have such a hold on society but thankfully are despised by the majority of good people.

A foolish faith in authority is the worst enemy of truth
Albert Einstein (1879 – 1955)

Four Secrets

Rape without Justice

I have settled well into my new position. I have definitely learned the ropes, having been thrown in at the deep end. The management team work in three shifts: morning, afternoon, and through the night, when one should always expect the unexpected. I am working the night shift, it's pumpkin time as the clock strikes midnight. I have checked the curfew signing out book; one of the young Greek stewardesses is missing!

Anxiously waiting, I am so very relieved, when I see her walk into my office in the middle of the night, although she appeared rather shaken to say the least.

"Are you okay Panni, I was worried about, you are a wee bit late?"

"Oh Miss Lesley, it's terrible. Please help me, I am so scared."

"Sit down my darling, you are safe now. Please tell me what's happened. Please, come and sit beside me. I will order you a nice cup of tea."

I waited till Panni was able to compose herself and gradually she revealed her terrible ordeal.

"Miss Lesley, I trust you, please, what I am about to tell you is a secret, because if anyone finds out I know I will be in so much trouble."

"Don't worry Panni, your secret is safe with me."

Still sobbing she started to tell me the terrible events that had just taken place.

"On one of my flights Miss Lesley, a Saudi passenger invited me out for dinner. He seemed so kind and was so interesting to talk to so I gave him my mobile number. This afternoon he called me inviting me to dinner at the beautiful fish restaurant on the Cornish. I accepted his invitation, he picked me up at 9 p.m. but instead of driving to the restaurant he drove me to an apartment?"

"Do you know his name?"

"Yes, it was Khaled."

"What about his surname?"

"No, sorry, I can't remember."

"That's okay," I said, as she started to sob. "Take your time Panni," I said, holding her hand, "it's okay you are safe now."

"He said that he had forgotten his wallet so we would drive to his apartment first to pick it up and from there go on to dinner. Oh, Miss Lesley, I realise now how stupid I have been. I shouldn't have gone with him."

"Did you recognise the area?"

"No, it's a place I have never been to, quite shabby and a little bit far away."

"Okay Panni, you are doing really well, can you tell me what happened next?"

"It was a small apartment, he asked me to have a seat and brought me a glass of juice, but when he sat down beside me on the sofa I started to feel very uncomfortable. I told him I was hungry and could we just go for dinner?"

"'Not yet,' he said putting his arms around me. 'Please stop!' I said. 'What? come on you little whore you know you want it.' I started crying. He became so angry and dragged me through to the bedroom throwing me on to the bed. 'Please stop' I pleaded. 'Shut up! he said. I started to scream, I was so scared, he hit me on my face and ..."

At this point Panni lowered her head.

"Oh, Miss Lesley, I feel so ashamed."

I held her hand.

"Panni, you have nothing to be ashamed about. He is a bad man. Now, please, when you are ready, can you tell me what happened next?"

"He pulled off my clothes and ..."

At this point again, she lowered her head.

"He raped me. Oh please help me, Miss Lesley, help me."

I hugged Panni and held her for some time, trying so hard to hold back my tears. I had to be strong for her sake, this was my job, but in my heart I thought, what a monster. I hope Karma bites him big time on the butt!

"How did you get back home Panni?"

"I ran out of the flat and just walked till I saw a taxi."

"Did you talk to anyone about this, security or the police?"

"No, Miss Lesley."

"I can send you to a doctor Panni and get a wee check-up."

"But Miss Lesley, does that mean you will have to report the matter?"

"Yes Panni, I will have to inform the head office and you know the police will then be involved."

"Oh Miss Lesley, if this gets out, they will blame me. They could arrest me for being in his company, couldn't they?"

"Panni, my darling, I know it is so unfair and wrong, but you know the laws here. Yes, you will be investigated by the authorities and being a woman will probably be blamed, and immediately your contract will be terminated."

"Oh Miss Lesley, I really need this job; I am helping my mum to look after my two little brothers."

"When are your days off?" I asked.

"Tomorrow Miss Lesley, I am going home to Greece for a week off."

"That's good my darling, you need some time away, are you sure you don't want to see a doctor Panni?"

"No Miss Lesley I will be alright."

"I am so very sorry Panni, you and I both know that it is absolutely atrocious that you will not be cared for or dealt with fairly here in this country, but the decision is up to you. We can either notify the authorities and try to find him, or you go back to Greece for your week off, perhaps see a doctor, get strong and try to forget this terrible experience. What do you think?"

"Miss Lesley I will go home."

"Okay, my darling, do you have a flight today?"

"Yes, Miss Lesley, I am supposed to operate a domestic flight to Riyadh and back."

"Don't worry; you are in no state to work today I will remove you from the flight, and prepare you a sick form. You can go to the medical centre in the morning and just say you have been feeling very sick during the night. Now go home, have a shower and try to get some sleep. It is over, you are safe, but if you need me I will be here in the office all night."

As Panni stood up ready to leave my office, I whispered gently to her:

"Remember it is our secret"

The pure and simple truth is rarely pure and never simple
Oscar Wilde (1854 – 1900)

Women of the Night

Like I was saying, a lot of mysterious things happen in the night. Hopefully tonight it will be quiet and all my girlies will come home safe. If at any time someone has not returned to the compound, I normally give thirty minutes leeway for any late arrivals. However, in that time if they have still not shown up then I must follow procedure. I visually check their apartment to make sure that they really are missing and just didn't forget to sign back in. God forbid there could have been an accident! OR?

Let me explain OR?

This is the part of my position that Nasser hadn't told me about. There is a small percentage of our flight attendants who don't fly very much, well hardly ever on commercial flights. They are known as the VIP girls. They sign out of the compound for a social event, and might be away for one night, one week or longer, depending on the request? Yes, you heard me right 'request'.

Tonight one of the Norwegian girls, Ingerid, hasn't yet returned to the compound. She is stunningly beautiful with fiery red hair and piercing green eyes. She left this morning at eleven o'clock. I know she is one of the VIP girls however I must follow the procedure, as one would do for any of the regular crews before writing a report that she is missing. This report is however not sent through normal channels, but placed in a red satchel that in the morning will be taken to the VIP headquarters and seen by Rony and Yaser. This procedure is followed every night until the VIP girl returns home. Sure enough two days later, in the middle of the night Ingerid arrives back to the compound and greets me in my office.

"Hello, Miss Lesley, how are you?"

"I am well, thank you Ingerid, and you?"

"Fine, thank you, Miss Lesley," she says, as she takes a seat beside me.

"Miss Lesley, I have been staying at the palace in Riyadh and look what the Prince gave me."

"Oh, you don't have to tell or show me anything," I said.

She whispered, "But the girls know we can tell you anything."

"Really," I smiled.

"Yes, Miss Lesley, do you know what they call you?"

"No" I said bemusedly, "but I think you are going to tell me anyway?"

"Yes Miss, you are known as the 'White Angel' because everyone in the compound respects you Miss Lesley."

I smiled, "Thank you, Ingerid."

"May I show you something?" she said.

"Yes of course," I replied, as she proceeded to open her bag and bring out a box from which she produced the most beautiful necklace. Its sparkling arrangement of emeralds encrusted in diamonds, truly magnificent, and from the bottom of her bag tucked neatly inside a pocket, she brought out a wad of money, equivalent to ten thousand pounds.

"You know Miss Lesley, I have a little girl back home and I am saving for her future. What I do is for my baby."

I smiled "You don't have to explain anything to me Ingerid, but something I am sure of is that you are a wonderful mum."

"Now off you go and get some rest."

"Thank you, Good Night, Miss Lesley."

"Good Night, Ingerid."

"If you judge people, you have no time to love them"
Mother Teresa

Please Don't Leave Us!

During the busy season of Haj, Saudi Airlines leases aircraft and crew from other foreign carriers. At this moment in time we have leased the crews from Canada, nicknamed Casi. There are about one hundred Canadian stewardesses at present in Saudi Arabia, living in the compound, working on a three-month stint. They are under the same regulations as our regular stewardesses. Their lovely manager, Marianne, will look after them. However, if any problems or issues arise with any of her stewardesses she will report back to my office. My goodness, midnight and all my girls are back home. Tonight thank goodness, I will not have to worry, or run around the compound looking for any lost souls.

Oops, spoke too soon! It's one o'clock in the morning ... the phone rings. It's Marianne.

"Hello, Marianne, how are you?"

"I have a problem Lesley; I will be in your office in five minutes."

"Okay, see you shortly."

Oh dear, I thought, this sounds serious. There goes my quiet night. I shouldn't have counted my chickens before they had hatched. Marianne entered the office with panic written all over her face.

"Please sit down Marianne, what's wrong, are you alright?"

"Not really Lesley, I have some stewardesses missing."

"What do you mean by some stewardesses? How many exactly?"

"You will never believe this but twenty-five are unaccounted for."

"Did you check their apartments?"

"Yes I did, and I asked some of their apartment mates if they had any idea where they were?"

"So, what did they say?"

"They said the word going round was that tonight there was a big party at one of the compounds where a lot of the Casi girls had been invited."

"Did you get the name of the compound?"

"No Lesley, no one seems to know."

"Okay Marianne, this is serious; I will call my Supervisor Gabrielle."

"Good Evening, Gabrielle, it is Lesley."

"Yes Lesley, gosh what time is it?"

"It's almost two in the morning, I am so sorry to wake you but I think we have a situation."

"What is wrong?"

"Marianne is with me and twenty-five of her Canadian stewardesses are missing."

"Okay Lesley, prepare a list of all their names."

"Already done."

"Okay, I will be with you shortly."

Ten minutes later Gabrielle arrived to the office. Poor woman, she had been working all day and now for sure she will be up all night.

"Any news, Lesley?"

"Nothing Mam."

Gabrielle turned to Marianne,

"Anything Marianne?"

"No, nothing, not a whisper."

"Right ladies, let's get the ball rolling. Start making calls!"

"Yes Mam, on it."

"And Lesley, please call the coffee shop and order a big pot of Turkish coffee and someone, please find me a packet of cigarettes. This is going to be one hell of a night."

"Yes Mam," I replied.

Dawn breaks, at last sunrise, it has been one long night, but after many calls, and cups of coffee, we finally locate our girls.

"Quickly Lesley, get your veil, thank God the girls have been found."

"Where are they?" I ask.

"They are in the main prison, allegedly there was a Muttawa raid at a party."

My heart leapt. "Oh no, not the Muttawa."

"Move quickly Lesley, you know what a hell hole that place is. We must get them out, the sooner the better!"

"Right boss," I said as we quickly put on our veils and left with the driver to get our girls!

Gabrielle, although very strict has a heart of gold. I respect her in her job and she knows that, like her, I will protect the girls, and won't take any harassment from anybody, especially the Muttawa. Arriving at the prison we are escorted to the cells. It really is a hell hole. Your heart would melt at the scene in front of us. The smells, filth and squalor would turn your stomach, like being in a seventeenth-century dungeon. Mainly black women from Africa are there, their babies and children cuddling up close to their mothers, they must have been so very frightened. What was their crime, you may ask? Well for many of them it would be simply an expired visa or perhaps begging on the streets to survive, having escaped abuse from a tyrant master. Yes, this is very much part of the society. There is no protection for domestic workers let alone women. They just don't have a leg to stand on. At the back of one of the cells I could see our girls huddled in the corner. What a scene, crimes against humanity to say the least.

We were promptly taken to the desk of the Saudi police chief. A man sitting behind a wooden desk smoking a cigarette; his swaggering manner, dishevelled uniform with brass apparel, and eyes like ice tore through your very being. I was disgusted by the way he looked and talked to us. I felt a shiver go down my spine. Gabrielle did the talking; she was so strong that even the Muttawas were silenced when she spoke. In another lifetime, she would have been a great Aung San Suu Kyi. As she conversed with the police chief, I was allowed a ten-minute visit with the girls in the cell. They hugged me and cried as I gave them some toiletries and water. A quick tally, all twenty-five were accounted for and, thank God, had been kept together.

"Keep your voices low girls," I whispered, "and tell me what happened?"

"Miss Lesley, take us home, please get us out of this prison."

"I will girls. We are working on it, try not to worry. Now please, I only have ten minutes, what happened?"

The girls were terrified.

"Please," I told them. "You must be strong. Please tell me now, in your own words, what happened?"

The clock was ticking.

One of the girls was eventually able to compose herself:

"We were invited to a party at one of the compounds. I don't remember where. We were enjoying ourselves, dancing and …." She became tearful at this point.

"Yes go on, was there any alcohol?" I asked her.

"Yes Miss Lesley, as usual, at every barbecue or party we have been invited to whether the hosts are Saudi or from another country, we are always served alcohol. It's just like parties back home in Canada."

"I am aware of that, now please keep your voices low. What happened next?"

"We heard someone shout 'Quick everyone out, it's a Muttawa raid.' Everyone was screaming, not knowing what to do or where to go. I ran upstairs and hid under one of the beds," she cried. "Miss Lesley, I heard someone enter the room, and stop near the bed. I was dragged by my hair from underneath the bed, he kicked and dragged me down the stairs, throwing me into a waiting truck."

Another one of the girls described how she tried to escape by jumping over the garden wall, but was pulled back down by another of the Muttawas and punched and dragged to the same truck.

"Right girls, I need you to be strong. I promise we will get you out soon, if not today, then hopefully tomorrow."

"Miss Lesley will they birch us?"

I couldn't tell them the truth, I knew it was a possibility if we didn't get them out quickly, away from these oppressors.

"No my darlings, you will be all right, I need you to be patient, brave and stay together."

"Oh, Miss Lesley, please don't leave us," one of the girls screamed, holding on to me.

"My darling, please let go," I turned to hug her. "I will be back soon!"

The ten minutes was up!

Gabrielle had her account from the police chief and I had my account from the girls. As we left the prison we conversed. To get these girls out our statements must be watertight. We returned to our office. The wheels were put in motion, all concerned departments, consulates, and VIPs notified. Tomorrow we must bring our girls home. Another twenty-four hours of wheeling and dealing and at last a positive outcome. I called Marianne.

"Mission accomplished – they will be released tomorrow; your girls are coming home."

"Thank God," said Marianne, "what happens next?"

"We are arranging to fly them out on the first available fight back to Canada."

"Thank you Lesley, to you and Gabrielle, their parents will be so relieved."

"Just another day at the office Marianne, Goodnight."

Termination of the Innocents

I am morning shift and so far nothing much is happening in the office, so I have decided to catch up on some paperwork while sipping some Turkish coffee. Ten minutes later the phone rings.

"Lesley, it's Gabrielle, I need you to collect passports from some of the flight attendants returning from their days off. I am faxing you a list."

"Why?" I asked

"I will call you shortly and brief you on the situation."

The fax arrived as I waited for Gabrielle's call. Five Arabic girls, Lebanese, Syrian and Palestinian were expected back from their days off, and their names were on the list. When I saw their names, I was rather puzzled. They are all professional and hardworking. I know them very well. Why have I to take their passports? Usually such a procedure means termination of contract, because of a misdemeanour. But I know these girls, they all have impeccable reputations. What on earth is going on? I could sense something was amiss! Twenty minutes later the phone rang. "Lesley, it's Gabrielle."

"Yes boss, what's happening?"

"Okay there are five names on that list which have been highlighted with a red marker, you must make sure you take their passports. Please confirm the highlighted names Lesley."

Confirming the names, I couldn't believe it.

"Gabrielle these are good flight attendants, lovely girls, what's happening?"

"Honestly Lesley, I am not sure what is going on but what I can tell you is; they are all from the minority Shia religion (branch of Islam)."

"What does it matter, they are such professional stewardesses, working hard to build a good life for their families. They are probably the bread winners in their family. Please, is there something we can do to help them?"

"Unfortunately, Lesley, this comes from the very top and there is nothing we can do."

"Och, Gabrielle there is always something we can do."

"Not this time Lesley, our hands are tied."

"Surely Gabrielle, someone will speak on their behalf."

"Lesley, you have an order, just take their passports and remove them from any flights."

It was a very tough morning, as my five beautiful stewardesses, smiling and relaxed, arrived back from their days off.

"We are back home Miss Lesley; did you miss us?"

"Always," I smiled. "Come girls, I need to talk to you."

"Of course, Miss Lesley."

We sat for one hour together as I broke the news to them. We hugged, we had tears.

"Can you do anything to help us Miss Lesley? We have done nothing wrong, we are not guilty of any bad doing. We haven't committed any crimes. We were just women who were born into the Shia religion. We are a peaceful people and have never hurt anyone."

"I know my precious ladies. I know how good and kind all of you are, but my hands are tied by those in authority."

How awful I thought. I know they must feel so alone, so betrayed. No one is helping them, they have been abandoned. They gave me their passports, we hugged for what would probably be the last time. Leaving the office one of the girls called Sarah turned to me with tears streaming down her face

"Please, Miss Lesley, isn't there anything you can do to help us?"

I got up and hugged her:

"Sarah, you are young and beautiful. You have great aviation experience, new airlines are opening up all the time and don't hold the same prejudice that we are unfortunately seeing here today."

"Will you give us a reference Miss Lesley?"

"Absolutely Sarah, for all five of you. Meet me tomorrow at 10 a.m. in the coffee shop and I will have your letters ready."

"Thank you, Miss Lesley," she said, as she left my office with the other girls, all knowing that their journey in Saudi Arabia had come to an end.

The hottest places in hell are reserved for those who
in times of great moral crisis maintain their neutrality.
Dante Alighieri (1265 – 1321)

Headhunted

Almost one year has passed and although the work is extremely challenging, with many ups and downs, I have most certainly enjoyed the position, especially the days when I know I was able to help someone and make a difference. Last night, I received a telephone call from one of the managers in the training centre a Miss Halima, asking if I would kindly meet her later today, when I had finished my shift, as she had a proposal that I might be interested in.

During the meeting with Miss Halima, I was offered the position of Instructor at the Training Centre.

"You know Lesley, your reputation proceeds you and I know you will be a great asset to our team, with the prospect of another promotion."

My goodness, it's so wonderful to be Head Hunted; it's pure magic! I have indeed accepted the position and I am about to start on another journey, another promotion, with so much experience under my belt and still in my 20's. I am sorry to say goodbye to Gabrielle and the position in the compound, but now I have to move on to the next level. However, she will always be one of my best friends.

The next day I met up with Miss Halima at the training centre. I have to say the training management are just brilliant. What a team. Mr Awadi the manager, himself being Saudi, is one of the kindest and most jovial managers I have known. Miss Halima, who is from Egypt, is so courteous, classy, and professional to a tee. My office is housed in a beautiful building of five levels, with its modern facade of magnificent glass windows creating an atmosphere of space, and elegance and with views of the old city. One of the perks of the job is that for one week every month I will operate a flight as a Safety Inspector, to the destination of my choice, with full expenses, relaxing in a five star hotel.

I have to say that although I enjoy all my classes, regardless of nationality, I have developed a soft spot for the young Saudi stewards in training who have so impressed me by their politeness and respect to me both as a woman and their teacher. I have built a motivational training package that I am now conducting with all levels, including management, throughout the Middle East, Asia, Africa, America and Europe. One more position with one more grade and I will be 'Top Gun'.

Desert Storm

I woke up this morning with my telephone ringing. It's another gorgeous sunny day, but who could be calling me at this time. It is so early, 6.00 am, and it's the weekend. Half-asleep, I pick up the phone.

"Hello,"

"Good Morning Lesley, how are you?" said the voice on the other end of the phone, a voice at first I didn't quite recognise.

"Who's speaking?" I asked.

"Oh my dear Lesley, have you forgotten your old friend?"

"Oh my goodness, is that you Charles?"

"Yes young lady, it is me, Charles."

I couldn't believe it was my old friend, a British Caribbean pilot whom I had met while he was still working in Saudi Arabia.

"Lesley, are you alright?"

"Oh yes, thank you, life is good."

"Actually Lesley, I am a little bit worried about the situation in the Gulf."

"What do you mean Charles?"

"Haven't you heard?"

"Heard what?" I asked, hearing an anxious undertone in his voice.

"The war has started. Iraq has just invaded Kuwait."

"Oh Charles, are you serious?"

"Never more so, the Gulf is at war Lesley. It's maybe time for you to get out?"

"Charles, this is serious."

"You bet girl, call the Embassy and find out the current situation, they will advise you on what to do."

"I will get right on to the Embassy now. Thank you so much for calling me Charles."

"That's okay Lesley, but please when you get a minute, call and let me know what's happening. Good Luck, dear friend."

"Thank you Charles, we will talk soon!"

My goodness, that was some wake up call. First things first, of course, make myself a much needed cup of coffee and then have a wee think and get my head around this before I call the embassy.

"Good morning, you are through to the British Embassy. My name is Nazir."

"Hello, my name is Miss Mitchell. I am a British passport holder working here in Jeddah with Saudi Arabian Airlines."

"How can I help you Miss Mitchell?" he inquired.

"Well Mr Nasir I have just had a call from a friend in America telling me that the Gulf war has started, seemingly Kuwait has been invaded by Iraq. Is it true?"

"Please hold Miss Mitchell," said the voice on the other end of the phone.

As I hung on, seconds seemed like eternity.

"Hello, is anyone there, please Nazir, are you there?" raising my voice at the silence on the other end of the phone. At last Mr Nasir was back on the line.

"Yes Miss Mitchell, there seems to be something happening, but we are not sure exactly what. Could you please call me back a bit later when hopefully we have some more information?"

"Call you back?" I said, in utter disbelief. "Mr Nazir, is the Ambassador there?"

"Please Miss Mitchell, call back a little later."

"But what should I do in the meantime?"

"Just stay where you are until I get more information, please!"

"Okay," I said, rather perturbed as I hung up the phone. I honestly feel after that telephone conversation; perhaps no one knows what is really happening. I am certainly not going to wait around here. I am going to call my good friend Gabrielle!

"Can I pop round now to your apartment Gabrielle? You will never believe the news I have for you."

"Sure Lesley, it sounds quite urgent?"

"Believe you me Gabrielle, it is. I will be there in about fifteen minutes."

As I quickly got dressed, it was such an incredible feeling; so many scenarios going through my head. Would I have to evacuate to the embassy, would bombs be dropping all around us, would we be invaded? I better get to Gabrielle's. Perhaps we will have to plan our own tentative course of action. Entering her apartment I am met by the delicious aroma of fresh Turkish coffee, which she was gently stirring as it bubbled away contentedly.

"Let's go through to the salon," she said, carrying the tray of coffee.

As she lights her cigarette, I start telling her the news.

"What do you mean Lesley, the embassy asked you to call back?"

"Some guy who answered the phone, probably one of the administration staff, asked me to call back. It sounded like they are not sure exactly what is going on. Let's put the television on Gabrielle, there might be something on CNN, you know how quick the Americans are at going live with a story."

As Gabrielle turned to CNN, one of their best known reporters, Christiane Amanpour, was reporting, as events were unfolding in front of us. My God Charles was right. We are at war!

"Oh my, this was a disaster waiting to happen, it has been on the cards for such a long time," said Gabrielle.

"Really?" I said.

"Oh Yes Lesley, there is a lot of discontent brewing in the Middle East and I am sure this is only the beginning. Excuse me for a moment Lesley, I am going through to my room, I will be back shortly, enjoy your coffee."

Five minutes passed; I called through to Gabrielle.

"Are you okay?"

From the other end of her apartment I heard her call.

"I'm okay Lesley. I am in the spare room, come through."

What is she up to I thought? As I entered the room, she stood with a broad smile pointing at a selection of empty suitcases on the floor.

"What are you up to Gabrielle?"

"Well Lesley," she continued to smile, "in case we have to evacuate, we should plan our escape. So, step number one, shall I use my Gucci, Dior or Chanel suitcase?"

"Well, Gabrielle," I said, as I bust out laughing, "you are right, for our getaway why don't you take the Gucci and I will follow with my Burberry. After all, a girl should always travel in style!"

The most wasted day of all, is that on
which we have not laughed
Sebastian Roch Nicolas Chamfort (1741 – 1794)

As events continued to unfold it was becoming clear to all, that apart from Kuwait, Saudi Arabia and Israel would also probably be in the firing line. The word on the street was that we were indeed in a terrible position. There was a high possibility of being hit by scud missiles in any chemical attacks. That afternoon I received a call from my Assistant Manager, Halima.

"Lesley, are you okay?"

"Yes Miss Halima, I am sitting with Gabrielle. Our eyes are glued to CNN."

"And you, Miss Halima, are you okay?"

"Yes, thank you Lesley."

"What do you think we should be doing Halima? I called the British Embassy earlier and I think they must still be gathering information, as they told me to call back."

"Well Lesley, don't worry, I called our boss Mr Awadi and he has asked that all of us from the training centre congregate there tomorrow at eight o'clock in the morning, as he will brief us on the latest developments and what steps we should now be taking. In the meantime, Lesley, I have received a fax that all aviation personnel should try to stay indoors, except for those on scheduled flights, until we are otherwise informed."

"Okay, thank you, Miss Halima, I will tell Gabrielle."

"Gosh Gabrielle, so much happening."

"Yes Lesley, I am going to get ready and go down to my office and brief my supervisors on the latest developments."

"Okay, I will go back to my apartment and call my family and let them know that I am okay."

"Hello mum, it's Lesley, how are you?"

"Oh Lesley, are you okay? Your dad and I were becoming so worried. The news about the Invasion of Kuwait by the Iraqis is all over the BBC."

"No please, don't worry mum, we are at least two hours away from Kuwait, so we are quite safe."

"Oh thank God, Lesley, here is you father."

"Hi dad."

"Hi Lesley, are you sure you are okay? We are watching the news, and they're talking about the Iraqis having chemical and biological warheads?"

"I know dad, but there are procedures being put in to place for our safety and we have an American military base here, so please don't worry. I will call you again tomorrow."

"Okay Lesley, we love you."

"Bye mum."

Next morning the training team met with Mr Awadi.

"Good Morning everyone, are you all here and accounted for?"

"Yes," shouted Saeed, one of the Saudi administration staff.

"Good," said Mr Awadi. "Salaam Alaykum, ladies and gentleman." (Peace to you all)

"Alaykum Salaam, Mr Awadi," (and Peace to you) we replied.

"Well, ladies and gentleman, I am sure you will be very aware of events unfolding in Kuwait. Hopefully, the allied forces will keep the Iraqis at bay by protecting our borders. So, at this moment, excluding of course Kuwait and its airspace, business will be as usual. However, after discussions I had last night with higher management and security, we must take some precautions in case of any deterioration in our current position.

Firstly, our lovely ladies, please ensure that you notify your respective Embassy of your contact information and status here in Saudi Arabia. Secondly, everyone must be aware that we have to be prepared in case of any sudden scud missile or chemical attack. So, we have been advised of the following:

When you go home you must seal around your windows and doors with thick duct tape in case of a gas attack."

As Mr Awadi spoke, I could hear my own heart beat and a chill run down my spine. Truth be told, I think we all felt the same.

Mr Awadi continued, pointing at the items on the floor in front of him.

"These gas masks I have in front of me are to be used in the event of a chemical Sarin gas attack. I will be passing them out to you shortly. Please remember, in case of an attack, don them as quickly as you can. However, ladies and gentleman, in the event of a mustard attack, immediately wash yourself down with soap and water as this type of attack will burn your skin. When you are at home, keep the bath full of water at all times, God forbid there is such an attack, then submerge yourself in the bath."

We all looked at Mr Awadi in disbelief, not knowing whether to laugh or cry.

He continued, "In the booklet which has been prepared for you to take home, please have a read as it will explain in more detail any further precautions you should be taking. Are there any questions so far?"

"Mr Awadi, with full respect, how will we know which gas it is?" I asked.

"Good question Lesley," he smiled.

Teasingly I said, "Perhaps they will give us some litmus paper so we can test the water before we jump into the bath?"

"Why would we do that?" asked Omar, one of my colleagues who, although a nice guy, wasn't always the sharpest pencil in the box.

"Well, I am no scientist, Omar, but if I remember, from studying Chemistry at school, if it turns blue it is alkaline and if red acidic."

"So what?" he said.

"Well, I don't know about you Omar, but if it is acidic, I am certainly not going for a swim."

There was a sudden uproar amongst the group. We all looked at each other in puzzlement, trying not to laugh.

Poor Mr Awadi, this is all the information he had been given at this time, and come on, let's face it, none of us are trained in military warfare. As the gas masks were passed around, it was soon realised that there were not enough masks for us all. One of the other Instructors, Ali, called out, "Where are the rest of the masks Mr Awadi? What are we meant to do, share one between two?"

"What do you mean by that?" asked Omar.

"Well," said Ali, "as you are one of my dear friends, Omar, we can share this one. You use it on Mondays and I will use it on Tuesdays."

Still the penny hadn't dropped. We all looked at poor Omar as he was still trying to make sense of what had just been said. Yet again, all of us, including our wonderful boss, erupted into such laughter joined eventually by poor Omar, who now at last understood the tongue and cheek nature of what was going on.

"Okay," said Mr Awadi, as we all composed ourselves.

"I will make sure that by the end of the day you all have a gas mask, before you leave the office. Inshalla we will keep safe and thank you all for your support at this critical time."

With loud applause we returned the gesture and thanked our much respected boss for being there for all of us.

Saddam Hussein tried and failed to shell Saudi positions and oil storage tanks. The first major ground invasion into Saudi Arabia took place in and around the city of Khafji, from 29th January till 1st February 1991; however, thankfully the city was recaptured by a Saudi Arabian National Guard battalion and Quatari tank companies, aided by coalition aircraft and American artillery.

The Secret of Happiness is Freedom
The Secret of Freedom is Courage
Thucydides (460 – 404 BC)

Thank God, we have all survived. The war has lasted six months, three weeks and five days. Today I am scheduled on one of the special flights to pick up Saudi soldiers returning from Kuwait to bring them back home. I am the only female within a team of three Saudi pilots and seventeen Saudi cabin crew, whom I will supervise. I feel so honoured to be asked.

"Good morning, Captain."

"Good morning, Lesley, how are you?"

"I am good thank you Captain. Sir, we have seventeen cabin crew on board and I have all the necessary paperwork. We have a stretcher fitted for one of the passengers on our return flight."

"Great, thank you Lesley. Let's close the doors and go pick up our boys."

"Okay, Captain."

As we started to taxi, I was feeling so very happy and so very proud that me, a girl from Glasgow, was being so highly thought of by my Saudi Arabian counterparts. Arriving in Kuwait there was a rush of pride as the crew welcomed our soldiers on board. Our brave stretcher passenger, bless him, showed all the signs of having been through the war. Everyone settles as we prepare for take-off, except for one of the passengers who appears very anxious and rather upset. Throughout the short flight we continually try to calm him down, but to no avail.

He has been continually rude to my crew and now as we are preparing for final descent in to Jeddah, one of my stewards, Samir, asks me to please come to the back of the aircraft as the man cannot be controlled.

"Mam Lesley, that aggressive man seated in my area is now standing up, being verbally abusive and refusing to sit back down and fasten his seat belt for landing. He is striking out at the stewards."

Quickly, I went back with Samir and requested the passenger, yet again, kindly take his seat for landing. He turned to me shouting with his hand waving at me in the air.

"Shut up sharmouta," (prostitute).

It was obvious to me that he was totally beyond talking to, so the last thing I wanted to do was antagonise him further; however, I must always protect my crew.

"Okay Samir, just leave him and take your jumpseat, we will be landing soon."

"But Mam Lesley, he is still standing."

"Leave him Samir and take your seat now," I said with raised voice.

I then informed the captain of the incident and sat down on a jump seat closer to the irate passenger so I could keep my eye on him. As we touched down and the aircraft speed increased momentum, he was still standing and shouting, but thankfully the increased speed threw him back onto his seat, without injury. When the plane came to a standstill I opened the doors to be met by security personnel and the police. The captain came out of the cockpit.

"Okay Lesley, as the passengers deplane, please point out the one who has been threatening your crew."

Seeing the burly figure approach, I whispered to the captain, "It is him sir."

"Right," he said, and within seconds the security had detained him.

After the last remaining passenger had deplaned the captain asked all the crew to gather at the front of the aircraft and in no uncertain terms the abusive passenger was asked to apologise to me and my crew. As he turned to me I knew his words meant nothing, but his face revealed the truth. He was one of those Saudi hard liners. So what did he think of me? I am a woman, an infidel, of no importance, hopefully our paths would never cross again. I pity his poor wife and daughters in their torment of living with such a man.

"I whispered to the captain."

"Thank you for standing by me sir."

"Well" he said, "you are one of us Lesley."

As the driver Mohamed took me home, I nestled down contently listening to my jazz CD.

"Did you have a good day Miss Lesley?" asked my driver.

"Oh yes, thank you Mohamed, just another day at the office."

Headhunted Again

Back in the Training Centre.

"Lesley, do you know a Mr Hani?" asked Halima.

"Oh yes, he was my manager in Frankfurt during my one-year stint there."

"Well Lesley, he is now the boss in our Paris office and I hear through the grapevine that he has been asking after you."

"Any idea why?"

"Seemingly he is having a few problems in the base, and he wants you to go there for a year or so to help him in his quest to motivate and train the crews."

"You mean leave here and go to live in Paris?"

"Yes there is nothing official, but this is what I am hearing. I know he is visiting Jeddah this week on a business trip, so please don't be surprised if he pops into your office."

"Gosh Halima, this is totally out of the blue."

"I do believe Lesley that his reputation precedes him and he would be a great boss to work for."

"Oh yes, that is true. He is very professional, kind and shrewd in the nicest sense. He is a go-getter and never gives up on a challenge."

Halima smiled, "I see Lesley, then you have a lot in common."

I laughed, "Thank you Halima."

"Well, we, the department, do not want to lose you, but if he does offer you the position and you do decide to go, then how about we call it 'on loan'? You will still belong to us, remaining under our umbrella, which means you will have the best of both worlds. You will be working in Paris, but your position here in training will be frozen, until you wish to return back to us. How does that sound?"

"Like a dream Halima."

"Okay," she whispered, "it is our little secret, for now."

Sure enough the next morning Mr Hani arrived at the training centre. No sooner had he arrived than he was in my office with the offer of a minimum one year in Paris. He is a very handsome man, always immaculately dressed with dazzling blue eyes and the most welcoming smile. From past experience, I know as a boss he is honest and dependable; its not just talk, he does the walk! Our meeting is fun and eventually develops into a sales pitch.

"So Lesley, what more can I say? I will give you anything if you come to Paris as one of my management team. You could supervise the base or be the Instructor of the base, whatever position you would like? Please, I need you to help me with the crews. I know they respect you so much. I am sure that you are aware, there are nine bases throughout the world, I need Paris to become the best, to be number one. So, please come to Paris and let's work together?"

"I do agree Mr Hani that I have the advantage of knowing most of the crews working out of Paris. I think the majority of them are senior with lots of experience. If I decide to take up your offer, I would be interested in the Chief Instructor position. May I say first of all that I am indeed honoured that you have asked me to join you in Paris. It's such a beautiful offer. However, there are a few things I need to iron out."

"Yes Lesley?"

"Actually Sir, I have three requests."

"Okay Lesley," he said with a mischievous smile, "what are your three requests?"

"Well Sir firstly, I will only work for one boss and that would be you. I wouldn't want anyone else from the base trying to pull one over me, telling me what to do or go to you behind my back. Every decision I need to make, any problem arising, I will always endeavour to keep you fully informed and of course sir` visa versa` on your part."

"Okay Lesley, I like that."

"Well it means, Sir, that in lieu of any office politics you and I will be singing from the same hymn sheet and that will give power to both our positions."

"Smart move Lesley, what about request number two?"

"Well at the moment I earn a good salary however as you know when I operate International flights as one of the Safety Inspectors, I earn much more. Therefore, my second request is that I operate one flight a month to Saudi Arabia, spending five days there. During my stay I will gather the latest updates on any new safety procedures and any gossip which would enhance your base in Paris. I will build you the best trainings, and increase your sales."

"Okay Lesley, sounds exciting, I agree."

"Now what is request number three?"

"At present I have a week off every month so that would have to continue. I usually go to Scotland to visit my parents. I have a house with them there."

"Yes I understand Lesley, but in Paris you will have every weekend off."

"Yes Mr Hani I know that, but I want the same privileges as I have in my present position."

He looked at me for a moment and then smiled, "Okay Lesley, my goodness you drive a hard bargain, but yes, your three requests are granted."

"Thank you, sir, then I look forward to working with you in Paris. I know, that together we can make Paris base No 1 worldwide."

In the evening back in my apartment I pondered over the days events. I had manoeuvred well, it was, I believe, a good outcome; living in Paris, earning more money, working ten days a month in the Paris office with a week in Scotland.

Two months later I was sitting in my office in Paris with my own training area, which mimicked a small movie theatre. The building is a beautiful tower called Tour Crystal, (Tower of Glass) standing high with its majestic glass façade overlooking the River Seine. As the sun sets across the urban horizon, such stunning views of illuminated barges and boats sailing through a city of magic, floodlit for the night.

I am living in a studio flat tucked away in the area known as Rue Du

Theatre, where at the end of its little cobbled road lies the most wonderful Jewish restaurant, where I often go with friends to chill out and relax in its cosy ambiance, with soothing music and delicious cuisine.

I have settled well in Paris. Next week I am off to Frankfurt to conduct a seminar with an audience of about one hundred and fifty Aviation personnel from around Europe; and guess what?

Paris Base has become No 1 worldwide.

Mission Accomplished, after one year and six months I am now returning back to mother base in Saudi Arabia.

I wonder what new challenges will await me there?

The City of Gold

"**G**ood morning Lesley, are you enjoying being back with us?"
"Oh yes Halima, absolutely."
"I love your new hair style Lesley."

"Thank you Halima, I just felt like a makeover and they do say that blondes have more fun."

"Well, keep me posted," she teased.

"I will," I smiled.

"Speaking of changes Lesley, day after tomorrow, I have removed you from some of your classes as you have been scheduled to operate a VIP flight."

"How can that be Halima?"

"We think the VIP is British but it is all very hush hush. It is definitely someone of high profile and a British passport holder has been asked to supervise the trip."

"Where to Halima?"

"They said one night stay over in London, but wouldn't say anymore, so please call the VIP office and find out further information."

That afternoon I called the VIP section.

"I believe you have scheduled me to supervise a flight to London the day after tomorrow?"

"Yes Lesley, our VIP is top priority."

"Who is the passenger?"

"Sorry I cannot tell you at the moment for security reasons, but what I can tell you is that she is female and the aircraft is a Gulfstream Lear jet."

"How many seats?"

"Only thirteen Lesley, and you only have a small group of passengers. You will be thoroughly briefed on the aircraft."

"Okay, I will be there."

What a mystery; who is the passenger?

The day of the flight I met up with two experienced British pilots and to my surprise the supervisor of the cabin was a young Saudi called Mohamed whom I had trained many years ago. A polite and charming young man. In my opinion a great example of the Saudi youth. Just as I was about to ask the captain who the passenger was when two well-dressed British men boarded the aircraft.

"Are you ready to depart Captain?" they inquired.

"Yes gentleman, whenever you are ready we will go."

"Great, our passenger awaits us in Dhahran. We would like to be in London early evening."

"Okay gentlemen, ten minutes and we will be on our way."

I followed the pilots through to the cockpit and asked,

"Captain, who is the passenger?"

"It's Mrs Thatcher. We will pick her up in Daharan. The two gentlemen on board are her bodyguards."

"Wow!" I said, "This is a turn up for the books."

How exciting. We are off to the epicentre of the oil industry, Daharan, to pick up the famous 'Iron Lady'.

"Here she comes," says her bodyguard.

As the limousines draw up beside the aircraft, it seems quite unreal, welcoming Mrs Thatcher on board. She has a lovely smile and gentle manner. Her dress code being quite appropriate for Saudi Arabia, wearing an elegant jacket and long skirt. We shake hands before Mohamed shows her through to the lounge at the rear of the jet, followed by her aide and then her son, Mark. Her two bodyguards take their seats near the front exit. Everyone is relaxing and in a happy mood as we serve a selection of drinks.

"Hello, what is your name?" asked Mrs Thatcher.

"I am Lesley, Madam, and the steward is called Mohamed."

"So lovely to meet you Lesley and you too Mohamed."

My goodness, every spare seat is busy with either luggage or hat boxes. At the last moment one of the most magnificent pieces that I have ever seen is being loaded into the cabin. An oasis set in Gold. A priceless work of art featuring a Bedouin village, with solid gold figurines set on top of a base of the semi-precious gem called Tiger's Eye, 6 inches thick. It was carried by four people onto the aircraft, and needed two seats and additional seatbelts to secure it. What a priceless gift from the desert, to a most remarkable lady!

During the flight Mrs Thatcher busied herself with paperwork and cat-napped. I had a wee chat with her aide who I could see had the deepest respect for her boss. What a memorable flight. Landing in London we say our goodbye's.

It is the dead of winter, frosty and cold. Stars sparkling like diamonds in the back drop of an ink blue sky. Camera bulbs flashing from the waiting paparazzi, as the limousines drive off with their precious cargo.

As the motorcade disappears from view, the flashing bulbs stop, and all that is left is an air of silence!

To feel valued, to know, even if only once in a while, that you can do a job well,
is an absolutely marvellous feeling

Barbara Walters
First female TV anchor (1929 –   )

Sleepless in Seattle

O h, how time flies, especially when you are enjoying yourself. I do hope that as you read through the pages, you too are enjoying this journey with me.

And, I hope you agree that it is just one big adventure that we are on. I have just got back from the VIP flight.

Halima has asked me to attend a meeting this afternoon about a business trip to Seattle with my Filipino colleague, Grace.

"Ladies," said Halima "you have been chosen to travel to the Boeing Aircraft factory in Seattle and be the first to have a peep at the new aircraft joining our fleet. It will be arriving soon to the kingdom."

"What type of aircraft is being delivered Halima?" I asked.

"Ladies you will both be part of a team who will be the first to view and learn about the world's first ever Boeing 747– 400 Glass cockpit aircraft, which carries around 434 passengers."

"That is big Halima."

"Yes it is Lesley, and on your return your objective will be to produce, write and design the cabin manual."

"What do you think ladies? I realise it is a big challenge, but higher management are convinced, as am I, that you are both up to it."

I looked to Grace, we both smiled

"I think it will be fun, let's go," whispered Grace.

"Yes," I said in a low voice, "I agree, great fun in Seattle, but it really will be one monster of a manual to produce. Our computer skills are not that brilliant, between that and our classroom trainings it will be such a huge challenge to meet deadlines."

"Trust me," said Grace mischievously. "We have never opted out of a challenge Lesley, so let's not start now, and anyway, I have a plan, a brilliant idea. I will tell you about it later, let's just both agree to do it."

"Okay," I said. "Seattle here we come."

Meeting adjourned, I joined Grace for coffee in her office.

"Right lady," I said. "Spill the beans. What plan of action do you have for us?"

"Well Lesley, between you and me, I was thinking that as soon as we return from the Seattle trip, we will both take a week off."

"Yes," I said, completely baffled.

"And then what?"

"We will get two first class tickets and fly to the Philippines, book a deluxe suite at a five-star hotel, where for the first couple of days we can work on the manual using the photo shots and script we collect in Seattle."

"Okay," I said.

"So far so good, and then what?"

"Well, then we will go to downtown Manila, to the university campus and hire an IT student who can compile the manual for us."

"Okay, and then?"

"Well, while the manual is being produced you and I can relax, enjoy ourselves on one of the islands and party."

"Great idea, Grace, but how much will all this cost?"

"I will use my 'wasta' (connections), I know a lot of people from the higher management at reservations. I will request two complimentary first class returns to Manila. The hotel has a great relationship with Saudia Airlines, so our stay there won't cost very much."

"What about the cost to produce the manual?" I said.

"Peanuts Lesley, it will set us back about 100 dollars. Just imagine returning to Saudi Arabia with a professionally designed manual, and way ahead of the deadline. Everyone will think it was all our work, it will be our secret."

"Cool Grace, I like your plan, naughty but nice, and actually it will be a win-win situation for all concerned."

"Exactly," agreed Grace. "So let's go shopping and start packing for our trip!"

What a wonderful two-week business trip to Seattle. At the Aviation Academy, viewing the world's first ever 747 glass cockpit jumbo jet, was absolutely fascinating. I am sure this business trip has given Grace and I the tools needed to produce a first class manual of this big bird. In our spare time, we so enjoyed sightseeing and visiting the finest seafood restaurants in town. We had no time to sleep, so much to enjoy, so we really were "Sleepless in Seattle!". Tomorrow, back to Saudi Arabia for our connection flight to Manila. Jet lag hasn't got a look in. From Middle east to America, now back to the Middle East and on to Asia as planned.

We have arrived in Manila and are relaxing in the grand suite of the famous Philippine Plaza, as we plan our agenda, both of us having the same belief, that one should work smarter rather than harder. So, for the next three days, we work 24/7, organising and writing the manual. We are enjoying room service three times a day, taking time to occasionally glance out of the window appreciating the stunning views of the Manila Bay. A majestic pool awaits us, surrounded by banana leaf and coconut palm trees. In the evening the scene becomes magical with lanterns, fairy lights, and soft melodies echoing through the night as guests are serenaded through dinner by Filipino maestros.

Day four has arrived, we are so upbeat having completed the hardest part of the task, producing the draft manual. Today we are off to downtown Manila to find ourselves a master in art and computer design at the university campus. We have to find someone who will accept our terms and conditions and use their magic to turn our work into a masterpiece. Arriving at the hub of the university campus we enter through an archway of a most fabulous building, as though we are in the Californian Silicon Valley.

"Mabuhay madam, (Hello in Tagalog) may I help you?" said a friendly young man seated at the reception desk.

"Yes," replied Grace, "We are looking for a student who has enough knowledge to produce an aviation manual according to our specifications and plans."

"Well mam I believe you have come to the right place. There is a student here called Roberto. He is a whizz with computer and design."

"Oh great! Is he here?"

"Yes mam, if you like I will call him to come and talk to you?"

"Yes that would be great thank you."

After a few minutes a well-groomed young man approached us.

"Hello ladies, I am Roberto. How can I help you?"

"Pleased to meet you Roberto, my name is Grace and this is my colleague Lesley. We have travelled all the way from Saudi Arabia, hoping that we could find someone to create an aviation manual for us in three days. We have already prepared a draft of the plans and now need a wizard to work some magic on the computer. We have been told that you could be the one. Are you interested?"

"Oh yes Madam, I certainly would. Please follow me through to where my computer is and I can look at your plans."

We followed Roberto to his open plan office and for the next couple of hours discussed our layout for the manual's design. It was obvious that Roberto was indeed an expert in his field and by the end of the discussion we were quite convinced that he was our man.

"Roberto," said Grace, "how much will your quote be for your work?"

Roberto blushed, "Mam whatever you would like to offer, I will be fine with that."

"We are very happy that you have agreed to produce our manual and for your work would it be acceptable to you if we offer you a payment of $100 American dollars for your time."

His face lit up in disbelief, "Oh yes indeed, mam, that would be very acceptable."

"Okay," I said, "Roberto, we will leave you now with the plans and return to collect the manual as agreed within three days' time."

"Thank you Mam, your manual will be ready and waiting on your return."

As Grace and I left the campus, happy with the outcome, we were now in a mood to celebrate.

"Let's go to China town and reward ourselves with some Dim sum."

"Oh yes Grace, I am definitely up for that."

We hailed a `calesa` (horse drawn taxi) and went off to have lunch at one of the most famous Dim Sum houses in Manila, accompanied by a rather expensive French wine, but what the heck we deserved it, our mission will soon be accomplished.

Next day after a good night's rest it was time to bring out our bikinis and party dresses. For the next three days we have a ball with all that sun, sand and Sangria!

On day four we return back to the campus and to our delight Roberto has completed the task. He hands us over the most professional work of art. A beautifully designed manual featuring the world's first ever glass cockpit aircraft manual, secure and snug in a floppy disc.

Brilliant!

We return back to Saudi Arabia, with disc in hand, six weeks ahead of schedule.

What praise we received on our return to the training centre. Yet again, another successful mission!

In the December of that year, Grace and I were invited back to Seattle in appreciation of our work and, alongside Saudi Dignitaries, we attended the most beautiful banquet ever.

Two days after Christmas our new 747 jumbo jet takes off from Seattle en route to Saudi Arabia, on its inaugural flight.

Grace and I are feeling honoured to be the first passengers on board, with an aircraft full of dignitaries as this special baby is flown home. Full media coverage is waiting as we touch down in Saudi Arabia aboard the world's first glass cockpit Jumbo jet. Such adulation from the waiting crowds with flowers and applause.

This is my Arabia - How Cool is this !

1997–2000
Top Gun

I was thinking that today would be a normal day in the office. I have some management courses to conduct this week, pertaining to the new aircraft; however, my Pakistani colleague Zafar, who conducts seminars in the male section for pilots and cabin crews has just called me.

"Lesley, my boss Captain Karim wants to talk to you."

"What about Zafar?"

"An opportunity has arisen in our department for a new facilitator to join our team and your name has come up."

"Gosh Zafar, I thought that any positions in your department was for males only. Does the Captain realise I am a woman?"

"Of course, he knows you are a woman, but your reputation precedes you Lesley, as you have the respect of all the men in the team. It is true if successful, you would be the first woman in history to hold such a prestigious position within a team of pilots and male facilitators."

"Gosh Zafar, this is unbelievable?"

Later that afternoon Zafar arrived to my office, I couldn't believe the news. "Lesley, Captain Karim wants to interview you sometime next week."

"My Godness, Zafar is this for real?"

"Oh yes Lesley, the team have all agreed and it is a once in a lifetime opportunity for you."

"But Zafar, what courses, if successful, would I be conducting?"

"It's a specialised field and the technical term is Crew Resource Management otherwise known as `CRM`. You will be studying airline fatalities caused by human error, and how they could have been avoided. You will also study the area of psychology, aircraft safety factors and listen to experts conclusions on voice recordings from black boxes which have been analysed and then re-enacted."

"Wow Zafar, what a mind-blowing, far reaching subject."

"If I was successful in the interview and joined the team, would there be a promotion for me?"

"Yes indeed Lesley, and you will be the first woman in Saudi history to attain such a position and your grade will be the ultimate."

"Gosh Zafar, this has always been my dream, to attain such a position, that means I will at last be Top Gun."

"So, are you on board Lesley?"

"You bet I am."

"Great, but please keep this news under wraps till after your interview. I will let the Captain know that you are very interested and I will get back to you with the interview date."

The next day I received a call from Zafar.

"Lesley, your interview will be in two days' time at 10.00 a.m."

Over the next couple of nights, I hardly slept. On the morning of my interview I could feel my heart palpitate as I waited outside the Captain's office. The secretary showed me through to the spacious office where Captain Karim and a panel of other male colleagues were waiting. The interview went very well. The Chief Pilot, Captain Karim commented on my impeccable work ethics and experience within the company. After the one-hour interview, the position was immediately offered to me. One of the best moments of my life. I felt so proud.

During the next few months I will be studying so many books and manuals relating to aviation safety and psychology, leading up to the big moment when I would be tested on my knowledge.

At last the big day has arrived for my dry run conducting a Safety Presentation in front of Captain Karim and the team. This is my chance. I already have lots of seminar experience that I have gained through the years, I just need to convince these guys that I am right for the team. Two hours later I closed the session. Now was the hard part, looking at the panel, waiting for their feedback. As they conferred, you could hear a pin drop.

Captain Karim spoke first.

"Well done Lesley, you certainly know your stuff. You conducted the seminar in an interesting and colourful manner. You certainly conveyed the message to us, your audience."

Then the American pilot spoke.

"Well done, you have covered all relevant safety, technical and human factor aspects."

My goodness, such positive feedback back from all of them. The only 'tongue in cheek' remark I got was from one of the facilitators who whispered in my ear,

"Try and keep your boobs away from the projector Lesley, otherwise the slides will be obscured."

"Yes Sir," I said smiling, hoping that this remark was just nothing to do with chauvinism!

Eventually I was proved right, the team I had joined were good guys and would stand up for me at any time. However, I think I already knew I would be okay, as I am a tough wee cookie. I had learned from an early age how to stand on my own two feet. That same day I am confirmed as part of the 'A Team'.

Although I had entered a man's world, I was always treated as their equal and as a lady.

I have achieved all my wishes, top position for a woman, great salary, owning a house with my parents in Scotland, having a lifetime retirement card to travel the world, and diamonds one can only dream of. I am truly independent and have made my parents proud.

No bird soars too high, if he soars with his own wings
William Blake (1757 – 1827)

Sandstorm (Haboub)

I t's a beautifully sunny, yet cool, November morning as the driver Mohamed takes me to the office. My pick up is normally 7.30 a.m. with a twenty-minute ride, which gets me there in time for coffee and any scheduled meetings before classes start. Mohamed is one of the kindest people you could meet. He hails from Pakistan, an older man, I would say in his sixties, tall and proud with the thickest white hair and matching beard. I have nicknamed him Papa Noel, to which we both laugh. Every morning I am greeted with a broad smile as he drives me to work, swapping stories about our beautiful homelands, my Scotland and his beloved Pakistan.

"You know Mam Lesley, I am an accountant back home and I have a small office still there."

"Oh my Papa, so what brought you here to Saudi Arabia?"

"Well Miss, I need to make more money so as to be able to send all my children to school and then college."

"You must so miss them and of course your lovely wife?"

"Oh yes, I talk to them on the phone as often as I can, but of course, I often wish I was with them."

"What type of contract do you have? When can you go back home for a holiday Papa?"

"Oh my, it is a two-year contract and still I have one year to go, miss."

"What does that mean exactly Papa, you cannot go home until you have completed two years with your company?"

"Exactly that miss, it will take me that time just to pay back the agent in Pakistan for finding me a sponsor here."

Listening to Papa I thought how lucky in life many of us are. Perhaps simplicity is the key, not too much fuss, just enough to be comfortable. I feel blessed, so happy to have been born in Scotland, lucky to have had a good British education and now be where I am at this moment of my life. Ten minutes into our journey and suddenly the sun disappears, it is so overcast. The sky has become a dark grey colour almost black in parts. The wind starts to howl and the sands start to stir.

"Gosh Papa, I think we have hit a sandstorm."

"Yes Miss Lesley, I am slowing down."

Minutes later we can hardly see in front of us. I have been in sandstorms before, but this one is so very different, so silent and eerie, as it folds its arms around us. Papa drives cautiously for the next twenty minutes, when at last we are in reach of the training centre. As he opens the door, I have to cover my face with my veil just to be able to breathe and not swallow the bellows of sand covering me, as I force my way through the blizzard and into my office, with Papa following. Entering the building, we catch our breath and brush ourselves off, poor papa I think has swallowed a pail of sand. (you see there are advantages to a veil).

"Well done Papa, you are a great driver, now please come up to my office and have a nice cup of tea and relax a while before you leave, let the haboub die down."

As I entered the office, the secretary Ahmed greeted me. "Good morning, Mam Lesley."

"Good morning, Ahmed, it is such a powerful haboub today. Papa and I were blown into the building."

"Oh yes, Mam Lesley, unbelievable and all our computers are down. We cannot check any of the flights. It is as though everything has been deleted."

"How can that be? Is it something to do with the sand storm?" I asked.

"We don't know. This has never happened before, but nothing is coming up on our computer screens."

Again the feeling hit me, something today is very wrong, I don't think it is just the sand storm? As the rest of my colleagues arrived to the office an announcement came over the tannoy:

"Would all instructors come to my office in fifteen minutes! All classes are cancelled until further notice."

"What's going on?" We were all so puzzled

"Where is Mohamed, the Instructor?" asked Ahmed.

"Oh he is operating a safety check flight to Delhi, so he won't be back to the office till tomorrow," replied one of the other instructors.

Mr Awadi opens his office door and invites all the training team in to his office, "Please take a seat everyone".

Our happy boss was looking so sullen, so drained. Looking through his office window, visibility is very low, it is so very dark. The car park and its vehicles have just about disappeared under a blanket of sand; it's like an omen, as though the end of the world is nigh!

"Ladies and gentleman, it is with great regret that I have to inform you that a short while ago Saudia flight A763 jumbo jet departing Dehli has crashed on take-off. As you all know our wonderful colleague Mohamed was on board. Unfortunately, at this point in time, we believe there are no survivors."

"Oh No! Not Mohamed!" someone shouted out.

He was newly married and expecting his first child, a real gentlemen and wonderful colleague. We all sat in disbelief, some of us cried and others were just silent. What had gone wrong?

Hours later the computers rebooted but Flight A763 Jumbo had been removed from the screen. We were all so dazed. How did a modern jumbo jet with 312 souls on board just crash? As the hours passed slowly the scenario was put together. It was sunset over Dehli when the aircraft was taking off and cleared at 30,000 feet by traffic control. A small charter Kazakh Airways plane was coming into land. The traffic controller saw two green blips converge and then vanish on his radar screen, the two planes had collided, there was no hope!

I did mention to you earlier in the book how wonderful the Saudi pilots are and to reinforce this fact an eye witness who was a resident in the dusty city of Dahni pahbot near to the crash site said:

"I strongly believe that the pilot of the Jumbo tried to save the people here in my village. We had a narrow escape."

Another of the village residents said, "I am sure the pilot averted what would have been a worse disaster by steering the blazing aircraft away from the village."

God Bless Mohamed and all those on board!

Miss Lesley, Help Me!!!

Gradually in the office we picked ourselves up, although daily as we walked by the empty office of Mohamed we were reminded of that fatal day. His name would be engraved on our hearts forever.

Life continues and I am enjoying my new position, busily working and conducting trainings between the flight deck section and the cabin attendant section. The plan is that I will be conducting trainings at six month intervals between both departments, depending on training and utilisation. This morning I have a meeting with Mr Awadi at 10.00 a.m., I wonder what it is about?

"Good morning, my sweet lady."

"Good morning, Mr Awadi."

"Lesley, I am receiving such good reports from Captain Karim and the team upstairs regarding your presentations in the safety department."

"Thank you, Mr Awadi."

"We need you to help us in this department for the coming six months as we have started a recruitment campaign. I realise that you have been working so hard with Captain Karim and thought it would be nice for you to take a break away from the office before you start training the new recruits next month. Why don't you go as a Safety Inspector on a check flight of your choosing to a sunny destination, relax beside a pool and feel pampered?"

"Actually Mr Awadi, that sounds a great idea."

"Great Lesley, I will schedule you, which destination would you like?"

"Oh, not too far."

"Well, what about Delhi?"

"Dehli?" I said, rather surprised, realising the flight number and route was the flight that had crashed only last month, with Mohamed on board.

"Yes," replied Mr Awadi, "we need to get back to normal. You can be our little diplomat," he smiled. "Listen to the staff in the hotel and chat with the friendly locals. Anyone who might approach you regarding the crash, please just let them know how the event has saddened us as a company. Although we were not held responsible, Chinese whispers and the media can alter opinion. We need some good publicity in that part of the world for people to trust us again."

"Mr Awadi, I thought I was going to relax?"

"Of course," he said, with a twinkle in his eye. "But just in case anyone approaches you, Lesley, you are our eyes and ears."

"Okay Mr Awadi, I will go."

One week later and here I am operating a check flight with seventeen cabin crew and three pilots. The air hostesses are multi-national and their cabin supervisor is Saudi, called Jawad. I have never been on a flight with him before, but unfortunately I have heard rumours that he is a bit of a womaniser; here's hoping that on this trip he behaves himself. About three hours into the flight one of the Filipino air hostesses, Joyce, approaches me.

"Mam Lesley, may I talk to you?"

"Of course Joyce, please have a seat."

"I am sorry, but the supervisor Jawad is behaving badly towards us at the back of the aircraft."

"What do you mean Joyce?" I asked?

"He is making lewd comments, especially at the Moroccan hostess Fauzia."

"Are you sure he is not just joking with you all?"

"No Mam Lesley, he is behaving badly and we have heard so many stories about him."

"Could just be idle gossip Joyce. Have any of you flown with him before?"

"Yes Mam, Fauzia flew with him last month and said he was acting in the same way, even after she told him to behave."

"Okay, go back to your station and leave it with me."

Gosh, everything was running smoothly and now this. I think that perhaps what people are saying about him probably has some truth. It seems so many people have heard the same rumours. No one seems to have a very high regard for him. I wonder why it has never reached the office? I will keep a close eye and if I see anything untoward, I will talk to him. If there is any truth in what I am hearing, then this is just not good enough for a man who is given so much authority.

A short time later I noticed Jawad speaking to the Moroccan flight attendant Fauzia in the galley and from the expression on her face it was obvious that she was upset. He suddenly puts his hand on her shoulder as though to comfort her and instantly she steps back. I have no idea what he was saying, but it is very obvious that whatever it was Fauzia isn't happy about it. He appeared angry and abruptly left the galley, disappearing to the first class area. Could these allegations be true? Is he so stupid to think he can act this way?

I went to the galley to have a coffee and a wee word with Fauzia, who was obviously still upset.

"Are you okay Fauzia?" I asked.

"Yes, thank you, Mam Lesley."

"Sorry, but I noticed that you were a little upset while the supervisor was talking to you. Is there anything I can help you with or anything you would like to talk about?"

Just at that moment Joyce appeared in the galley.

"Don't be scared Fauzia, tell Mam Lesley what's been happening."

Fauzia looked at me, "the supervisor never leaves me alone Mam Lesley. I flew with him before and he is always pestering me. He keeps saying he wants me as his girlfriend. I am sorry but he is a real creep."

"You have nothing to be sorry about Fauzia."

"I didn't want to say anything to anyone in case I lost my job."

"It's alright Fauzia please don't worry. You are not going lose your job. Has he ever threatened you?"

"No Mam Lesley, he is just so sleazy and I am scared, as are many of my friends who have flown with him. We heard that he raped a girl on one of the flights."

"Why has no one reported what he is doing?"

"Because he has wasta (connections), which of course mam Lesley, as you know, in the Arab world means that he is well protected."

"I understand, Fauzia, what you are saying, but these are serious allegations."

"Oh please Mam Lesley, I know, but it is the truth."

"Don't worry Fauzia, you will be okay. If at any time during this five day trip he approaches you in any way that you feel threatened by, please let me know immediately."

"Yes, thank you, Mam Lesley, I do trust you, as I know all the girls do."

"Good Fauzia, well, let's get back to work."

I turned, "And you too Joyce, are you okay with that?"

"Yes, thank you, Mam."

"Good, young ladies, the seatbelt will be coming on for landing shortly so please start to prepare your cabin."

Returning to my seat in first class, I realised that at some point during the next five days I would have to talk to Jawad and hear what he had to say, after all there are two sides to every story. I think perhaps on the return trip to Saudi Arabia would be a good time to have an informal chat with him.

As the seatbelt sign went on for landing my thoughts turned to my wonderful colleague Mohamed who only a month ago lost his life on this same journey. What were his thoughts? Probably like mine; looking forward to a relaxing stay in a beautiful destination. But, I still have an uneasiness, just like I had the day of the sandstorm. Something is bugging me, something isn't right!

The passengers have deplaned and the crew board the comfortable air conditioned bus, to take us to our five-star luxury hotel. Thank goodness for the air conditioning as the outside temperature is about 68 degrees. I have operated so many trips to Dehli. Such a cosmopolitan city due to the multi-ethnic and multicultural presence of the vast Indian bureaucracy and political system.

The Captain has kindly invited all the crew tonight to dinner. I am so looking forward to a good sleep in the luxury suite that I am always given while here. Tomorrow I will probably relax by the massive pool before taking a rickshaw ride through the old city and be transported back 400 years. Glide through the streets of agricultural marvels, multi-coloured facades, beautifully decorated shops, traditionally dressed men and women in a surge of colour, and the smells and tastes from poppadum eateries that line the historical alleys. India has so much intrigue and mystery. Its people are so welcoming and warm, even though so many are poor and try to survive on a day to day basis. They would give you their last piece of bread. As one views the landscape from the comfort and luxury of the hotel, depending on which way you turn, in one direction the mansions of the so called elite and in the other direction, cardboard boxes which the poor and untouchables call home. Two different worlds trying to coexist; the haves and the have not's.

How lucky I am, yes, I have to work hard for it all, but at least I had the opportunity, unlike so many!

We arrive at the hotel and, just as I thought, my room is a deluxe suite but you will never guess who is on the same floor as me and their room directly opposite, none other than the flight supervisor himself Jawad!

All the crew meet a little later in the beautiful foyer of marble with the most stunning displays of fresh flowers. I am so looking forward to this evening and the next five days of thinking about nothing except food, wine, music and lots and lots of sleep. After dinner, and quite satisfied, we make our way to our respective rooms.

"See you tomorrow Mam Lesley, by the pool," said one of the crew.

"Absolutely ladies, good night."

The last ones left in the lift are myself and Jawad as we are sharing the same floor, situated above the rest of the crew.

"I arranged that suite for you Lesley," he said, "I thought it would be nice that you are near me."

I felt a shiver go down my spine. Was it because of the rumours or was it his manner? I cut him short "Actually Jawad, I am always given a suite on this floor."

He ignored my remark, "Would you like to join me in my room for a drink?" he said, as we reached our rooms.

"No thank you, Jawad, I am quite tired and plan an early start tomorrow. Goodnight," I said, as I used my electronic key card to open my room door, and without any delay banged it closed behind me. This guy is a real sleaze. Call it intuition but I feel that he is not the `full shilling`.

As I got ready for bed, there was a knock at my door. Thank goodness I didn't open it, instead I looked through the peephole and guess who was there, knocking on my door, none other than Jawad. I ignored him and said nothing. He knocked a few more times and then suddenly stopped. Nervously I looked again through the peephole. There was no sign of him. Where had he gone? I slipped into the gigantic double bed between the crisp clean sheets and before long I had dosed off. I am not sure how long passed but some time later I was woken up with what sounded like a woman's screams

"Miss Lesley, Help me!"

My room was in darkness. I sat up and fumbled, reaching for the bedside lamp. The screams had stopped, there was nothing but absolute silence. I must have been dreaming. I got up and looked again through the peephole. No one was about, I must be really tired. I went back to bed and snuggled under the sheets. I really don't know how long I was asleep before my phone rang. It was still very dark outside. It must be the middle of the night as I stretched to find the phone. I am so very tired, who is calling me at this time?

"Mam Lesley, it is Carmen, one of the crew, please help us. I am with Rosa and she has been raped by the supervisor Jawad."

"What!?" I said, as I sat up, wondering what the hell was going on.

"Please take your time Carmen, where are you?"

"I am in the room with Rosa. She is hurt and crying."

"Okay Carmen, which room are you in?"

She gave me her room number.

"Both of you stay where you are, I am on my way down."

Oh, what a night, what's going on, I thought, as I changed quickly into my jeans and rushed to the lift to get to the girls' room. What a scene, Carmen was sitting in tears and lying on the bed was Rosa, a Syrian Christian girl, only twenty years old, not long out of training. She was a quiet natured girl, with a kind disposition and someone who wouldn't say boo to a goose.

"Oh Rosa," I said as I held her tight, "what's happened?"

"The supervisor attacked me in his room. Oh, Miss Lesley, I am a good girl."

"I know you are Rosa; you are safe now. Carmen would you make a cup of tea for Rosa please."

"Yes, of course, Mam Lesley."

Looking at Rosa, my heart broke. She was such a slender girl. Her face and arms were swollen and bruised, and a chunk of hair was missing from the back of her head. I sat down beside her and held her close.

As Carmen sat to comfort Rosa I starting making calls. First to the hotel manager, to get a doctor to the room as quickly as possible saying "One of the crew is very poorly."

As we waited for the doctor to arrive, Rosa began to tell me what had happened.

"As I lay in my room the phone rang. It was the supervisor Jawad telling me that our flight departure had changed, therefore our stay in Delhi had been cut short. He then said that the all the crew were to meet now in his room for a briefing as we would be departing very early in the morning. Oh Mam Lesley I feel so very stupid, but I thought it was for real."

"It's okay, Rosa, it does happen on occasion that flights change with quick turnarounds and sometimes we do then gather in the supervisor's room for a briefing. You are anything but stupid, so please, carry on."

"I went to his room and he offered me a drink. I told him that I didn't want anything and where was the rest of the crew?"

"'Don't be silly, there is no crew coming, I just wanted to spend time with you,' he said."

"He started to touch me Mam Lesley, I felt so scared and asked him to stop but,"... she hesitated, close to tears.

"It's okay Rosa, take your time."

"He just wouldn't stop, so I ran for the door. I managed to get out of the room and ran along the corridor to where the lifts were, but he ran after me. He caught me and dragged me by my hair back along the corridor to his room. I screamed for help Mam Lesley, I called your name, but you didn't hear me. No one did. ..."

At that point my heart missed a beat, my God, I was thinking, it must have been Rosa calling me for help when I heard the scream, it hadn't been a dream after all. Oh no, if only I had realised, if only I had opened my door!

"Do you want to stop Rosa, or can we carry on?"

She composed herself.

"No mam Lesley, I am okay, I will carry on. As he dragged me back into the room he bolted the door behind us. I pleaded with him to let me go. He pushed me on to the bed, I struggled to get away but he was too strong and started to hit me, so I just stopped struggling because I didn't want him to hurt me anymore."

She screamed, "He raped me, Mam Lesley."

The poor wee thing, I just held her as I looked at her wee body, it was obvious that she was saying the truth because apart from her terrible condition, with multiple bruising and swelling on her face, arms and legs and a huge chunk of her missing from where he had dragged her screaming back to his room, I myself can testify to have been woken up by her screams and calling my name. If it's the last thing I do, I am going to get justice for Rosa and get this vile man locked up. As they say the `proof is in the pudding` and after these events and the whispers going round about him, I will make sure that this pudding gets baked!

"How did you get away Rosa?"

"I lay still as he went to the bathroom. I realised that perhaps now was the time to try and run away. I got up from the bed and ran towards the door. Thank goodness I was able to unbolt the lock, the door opened and I just ran."

There was a knock at the door. "Okay Rosa, let me open the door it is probably the doctor."

"Good Morning, Doctor, please come in."

"Good Morning," he replied.

He was a middle aged Indian gentleman, smartly dressed in suit and tie. He spoke politely and listened attentively as I explained the alleged events that had taken place.

"Can you please examine Rosa, doctor?"

"Of course I will, but the police will have to be informed."

"Yes of course, I am just going to inform our Captain and my liaison in Saudi Arabia before calling them."

As the doctor examined Rosa, I called and informed the Captain of the situation. At first he was so saddened by what was happening yet at the same time one could sense his anger and disbelief that one of our team could be so depraved.

"Have you informed the police yet Lesley?" he asked.

"No yet, Sir, the doctor is here as we speak. I am going to call my counterpart in Saudi Arabia to make them aware of the situation and then I will inform the police."

"Do you know where Jawad is at this time Lesley?"

"No Captain."

"Okay, I will follow up on him and I will tell him to stay in his room till further notice."

"Thank you, Captain."

"Good job, Lesley, I am here if you need me. Just keep me in the loop."

As I hung up the phone the doctor confirmed that Rosa had indeed been through an ordeal.

"I cannot give Miss Rosa an internal examination but it is obvious that she has been badly assaulted. I would suggest that you inform the police now of the incident and I can make arrangements for her immediate transfer to hospital for a thorough check."

"Thank you Doctor, I will inform Saudi Arabia now of the incident and your recommendation."

"This is my card with my number Miss, please call me as soon as you can."

"Thank you, please would you keep this incident confidential until the police have been informed?"

"Of course, Miss."

"Thank you again, doctor, for your discretion."

As the doctor left the room, I reassured Rosa, that she would be okay and that I would be with her all the way. At this point I called my counterpart and best friend Gabrielle in Saudi Arabia, who you have already met earlier in the book. She is trustworthy, all about justice, and doesn't take prisoners!

"Do you believe Rosa's story Lesley?"

"Absolutely Gabrielle, I myself heard her screams for help and the doctor has confirmed that it is obvious that she has been through an ordeal! Rosa has asked that I inform the police and then I will accompany her to the hospital for a full examination."

"Okay Lesley, give me ten minutes and I will inform our VIP Head of Legal Affairs and get back to you as soon as possible."

As she had promised, within ten minutes she had called me back.

"Lesley I am going to pass you over to Mr Yaser, Head of the VIP section."

"Hello Lesley, this is Mr Yaser."

"Good Morning, Sir."

"I have been briefed by Gabrielle about your situation. I am sorry for the stewardess involved."

"Yes Sir she is rather shaken up, as you can imagine, but putting on a brave face."

"What is happening at this minute?"

"The doctor is waiting for my call and then we will be transported to the hospital. However, before that we need now to inform the police."

"Right Lesley, this is a very sensitive situation, please do not leave Rosa's side, call the police now and be with her at the hospital."

"Of course Mr Yaser."

"Our country manager for India, a Mr Khalid, will fly from Bombay today and be with you at some point late afternoon. I know you can handle this Lesley; we are depending on you. I also need you to try and keep the story out of the media. Having lost an aircraft last month, publicity like this will not be in our favour as you can imagine."

"Yes Sir, I do realise that, I will do all I can to keep a lid on it."

"Thank you Lesley. Rosa is our priority, please make sure she has everything she needs."

"Of course, Sir."

"Good, I will check in with you a little bit later. Ma Salama, Lesley."

I called the police and within minutes they arrived. Two male police constables in khaki uniforms and berets armed with lathis (batons). I explained what had allegedly happened to Rosa. Their English wasn't fluent but we all understood each other and they were quite emphatic towards us as they took our statements. However as in Saudi Arabia I feel India is a man's world and, of course, for such a sensitive situation, I would rather it had been a female officer, but that was not to be the case.

Outside the hotel a two-seater police jeep was waiting. I helped Rosa into the front seat, while I climbed up into the back of the jeep, where a third police man was waiting, armed with what looked like an assault rifle. I sat opposite him, giving him a quick nod, and hoping that this would be one short, quick trip. As we sped away I looked up at the most beautiful star-filled ink blue sky, thinking, what am I doing here? What a relaxing trip to Delhi, wait till I get hold of my lovely boss Mr Awadi! We arrived at a government hospital which was like something out of the blitz. Allegedly, a small private plane had crashed that very night. Doctors and nurses were scurrying around with trolleys and bags of blood. Nothing seemed very clean nor sterile, and stagnant smells filled the air.

Poor Rosa was asked to lie on a trolley within a cubicle, literally parked beside a blood splattered wall. However, I have to be fair, the kindness, empathy and care given to Rosa by the doctors and nurses was second to none. After a thorough examination, and some tests, there was a consensus amongst the medical team that Rosa had indeed been raped. Through it all I was so proud of Rosa, after such a terrible ordeal she was still managing very well, trying to be so very brave. My heart was breaking for this wee soul, I myself so wanted to cry. This is such a traumatic situation but I must stay strong for her.

The coolness of the night had given way to the heat of the morning sun. Rosa was shattered, and I just wanted to get her out of the hospital and back to the hotel where she could have a good rest. However, the police explained that we would now have to go firstly to the police station for Rosa to read over and sign her statement, as only then they would be able to bring Jawad into custody.

At the police station we were taken to the office of the police Inspector. He was quite a big, burly guy, looking very dapper in his uniform. He greeted us kindly, inviting us to take a seat by his desk. He asked his secretary to make some tea for us, before starting to ask Rosa questions. The tea arrived and can you believe it, in a police station on the outskirts of Delhi being served tea from a beautiful porcelain tea pot engraved with pink roses with matching cups and saucers. What one would rather expect at an afternoon tea party on the lawn by the lady of the manor, certainly not by the Chief of Police in India. As it happens, I am actually not a tea Jenny, as you will probably have surmised from previous chapters. I am more of a coffee person, but oh dear the Indians do so enjoy their tea; milky and with so much sugar that the teaspoon had become emerged in the sticky mass. Of course, it was very kind of the Inspector to look after us this way, therefore, trying to be polite, I accepted a cup from him, although politely declining another.

As the Inspector questioned Rosa it was obvious that she was exhausted physically, mentally and emotionally and needed to rest.

"Sir, if you don't mind I think Rosa is just too tired to answer any more questions. May I please take her back to the hotel?"

"Of course, Miss Lesley, just another five minutes and then I need Rosa to sign the statement."

"May I read the statement before Rosa signs Inspector?"

"Of course miss."

I read over the statement with Rosa. It was very specific and accurate. As Rosa signed, the Inspector informed us that Mr Jawad would now be taken into custody. Hopefully, I thought, justice would now be served. The police dropped Rosa and I back at the hotel before going onto arrest Mr Jawad and take him into custody. I took Rosa back to her room, where Carmen was waiting for us.

"Please Rosa, have something to eat from room service and then try to get some rest. You are a very brave lady and you have done the right thing in pressing charges. Hopefully, we can prevent Jawad from ever hurting anyone else."

"I will stay with Rosa," said Carmen.

"Thank you Carmen, that would be lovely. Rosa you must try and get some sleep. I will pop in later this evening, but in the meantime if you need anything just call me, it doesn't matter what time it is."

When I got back to my room I ordered room service and started making calls.

"Captain, it is Lesley, just to let you know that Rosa is well and back in her room but, as you can imagine, utterly exhausted after her ordeal. Tomorrow morning, we have to return to the police station for any new evidence and updates. The supervisor, Jawad, is in custody, pending a full investigation. I am now going to call Saudi Arabia and give them an update."

"Great Lesley, but you too must be exhausted, have you had any sleep?"

"No Captain, I am okay; however, I am sure that I will sleep like a log tonight. I will get back to you with any updates."

No sooner had I put my head on the pillow than the phone rang; it was the Country Manager just arrived from Bombay.

"Salaam Lesley, I am Siraj, the Country Manager of Bombay, can you come to my suite in about thirty minutes for a briefing?"

"Yes Siraj, I will be there."

I am so tired. Hopefully, a quick shower and a Turkish coffee and I will be as good as new.

"Salaam Alaykum, Miss Lesley, please come in. I am Siraj the Country Manager."

Yet once again, I had to explain the chain of events leading to the current situation.

"The most important thing at this point in time Siraj, is that Rosa is safe and that Jawad is now in custody, pending investigation."

He looked at me with a puzzled look and seemed rather distant. I honestly thought he would tell me that he would now take over, but oh no, not a hope in hell. Instead he tried to whitewash the situation and for some reason try to brush me off.

"I will let you know what Saudi Arabia's intentions are Miss Lesley after I have discussed the situation with them."

"Discussed what exactly, Siraj?"

"As I have said, I will let you know."

"Very well, I will return to my room, get some rest and wait for your call."

What a male chauvinist I thought. Absolutely 'Zift' (useless). Why has he flown in from Bombay, I have no idea or maybe I do? I think, on hindsight and my gut feeling, it will be better for Rosa, if I take the lead and not this specimen of a man.

In the evening the VIP, Yaser, called me from Jeddah.

"Tomorrow Lesley, when you go to the police station with Rosa please suggest to the police Inspector that your management in Saudi Arabia are requesting that both Rosa and Jawad be allowed back to Saudi Arabia on the first available Saudi flight, where justice will be served."

"But Yaser, what if Rosa wants him tried here?"

"Then Lesley, explain to her that it would be better for her to be back here in Saudi Arabia for justice to be served. This request Lesley, comes from the very top, from the Royals. Jawad is from quite a big journalistic family. He could buy his way out of a Delhi jail, but here in Saudi Arabia if the pending evidence proves his guilt, then justice will be swift."

"Do you promise Yaser, if proven that he is guilty, no blame whatsoever will be on Rosa?"

"I promise Lesley."

"Then Yaser, that is good enough for me. I will talk to Rosa tonight before we meet with the police in the morning."

"Thank you Lesley, you are doing a good job. One other thing, try and keep the story away from the media, as I mentioned before, and as you are already aware we are on their radar from the crash. Now a Saudi allegedly committing rape in Delhi, is not going to help us either in the domestic or political arena."

"I understand Yaser, like a stealth aircraft, I will be in and out."

Later that night I went down to visit Rosa. She was a wee bit brighter, but Carmen said she had hardly slept. I sat and took my time with her, giving her the options on the decisions she would have to make.

"Will they blame me, Mam Lesley?"

"Absolutely not."

"When you went to his room, as you have told the police, you thought there was a briefing?"

"That's right, Mam Lesley."

"Well Rosa this is a practice which our airline sometime uses, especially in countries that don't have much of a briefing room, so Jawad tried to use this practice to his advantage. He lied and got you to his room under false pretences. He is evil Rosa and needs to be shut away. I know that Saudi Arabia is a man's world as I do believe is India, but this terrible crime that has been committed has reached the highest position in Saudi Arabia and there will be no sweeping it under the carpet, not if both of us stay strong."

"Oh thank you, Mam Lesley, for standing by me."

"I am standing by you Rosa because you have been very wronged. Jawad has to be dealt with and held accountable for what he has done. So, do you agree that we all go back to Saudi Arabia together, where he will face the punishment he so deserves?"

"What do you think, Mam Lesley?"

"It's not up to me Rosa, it is your decision, but if it was mine, I would go back. He comes from quite an affluent media family in Saudi Arabia. I am sure that with one call they could buy him out of a Delhi prison and honestly we don't know how long it would take before the case comes up in court, so you would be stuck here, whereas back in Jeddah you are in a familiar environment and I have been guaranteed, from the top, that they will protect you, and with the evidence that they have gathered so far Rosa, the finger is so pointing at him."

She looked at me and smiled, "Yes Mam Lesley, let's go home and let him face the music there."

"If this is your final decision Rosa, tomorrow we will inform the police and I will make all the arrangements to bring him back with us to Saudi Arabia."

"Thank you, Mam Lesley."

"I will leave you now and tomorrow let's meet for breakfast in the coffee shop at 8.00 a.m., which gives us enough time to go over any questions you may have or anything you are still unsure about, before we go to the police station. One last thing ladies, that I must mention, is please, do not discuss with any of the other crew members what has happened. If any of them ask why you are not joining them for any of the activities, then Carmen you just say that Rosa is not feeling very well and has decided to stay indoors to relax. and that you are keeping her company."

"Okay," said Carmen, "I will do that, Mam Lesley."

As I got to my room, I poured myself a wee glass of wine. I have been awake about thirty-seven hours and feel exhausted, but thank goodness, Rosa will be okay, and for sure tomorrow will be another big day. I am so hungry and tired, not sure whether to eat first or just sleep? Oh let me call room service, I think a tasty cheese burger and fries will suffice, before I doze off to the land of nod.

The next morning, I woke up early, around 6.00 a.m., but I really did have a sleepless night, so much on my mind, so much to do. I have decided to go for a relaxing early morning swim, before joining Rosa at eight in the coffee shop. Such a beautiful pool, the early morning sun was starting to heat the water as I dived in and slowly came back to the surface, feeling so invigorated as I gently swam to the other side of the pool. So quiet and calm, no one was around except hotel staff preparing the bed loungers around the pool. Turning on my back, I just floated, the water lapping gently around me as I looked up at the most beautiful blue Indian sky. The warmth of the early morning sun felt so good as it covered me like a blanket, so relaxing, so calming as I closed my eyes for a couple of minutes, oh how lovely. This is how I was supposed to spend my time in Delhi. not in a downtown police station, but then again what would have happened to Rosa if I wasn't here, it was meant to be! It's eight o'clock and Rosa is already waiting for me in the coffee shop.

"Good Morning Rosa, how are you feeling today, did you manage to get any sleep?"

"Not really, Mam Lesley, one of the pilots called me, it was the Saudi flight engineer called Rashid."

"What did he want?" I asked.

"Well, he asked me what had happened. Seemingly Jawad at some point before the police took him into custody had called Rashid telling him that there had been a problem, that he was sorry and wanted to talk to me. Rashid then asked me what had happened, but as you advised Miss Lesley I didn't tell him anything. He then asked me if you knew what was happening, so I told him, 'Yes.' "

He then said, "Look, Jawad has said that it will be better for you just to forget what happened and tell no one."

I gasped in horror, "Oh Rosa, was he threatening you?"

"I am not sure, but I am feeling so scared."

I hugged her, "Rosa I will deal with them. I am with you all the way. You are in the right, he is guilty and a bully. This is his final trump card, to try and unsettle you but we are not going to allow him to do that, are we?"

"Oh no, Mam Lesley, he is so guilty of this terrible crime against me and I know you will always be there for me."

"Well then, let's have our breakfast. Today will be our day; we will get him."

Just as we were finishing breakfast, I could see from the corner of my eye the flight engineer Rashid sitting at a table in the foyer with some other Saudi guys that I didn't recognise. I got up from the table.

"Excuse me Rosa, relax with your coffee, I will be back in five minutes."

I approached Rashid's table, greeting him "Salaam Alaykum," asking that he join me at the next table for a quick word.

"Of course Lesley," he said, standing up and joining me at the other table.

"How are you?" I enquired.

"I am fine," he said, with bit of a sullen undertone.

"I think you are aware Rashid that a serious problem has arisen between Jawad and one of the stewardesses, whom I believe you called last night."

"Well yes I did, I don't want her blabbing her mouth to everyone."

"Listen carefully Rashid, she is not blabbing her mouth to everyone. Please do not call or approach her again, at any time during our stay in Delhi."

"Who do you think you are?" he said.

"Who am I? I am the one who has been put in charge of the cabin crew at this point in time, per the highest authority back in Saudi Arabia. I am the one who will be taking care of Rosa and Jawad, so please do not try to interfere."

"You have no right to try to dictate to me," he said.

"On this occasion I have every right Rashid, and if you try any more stunts as you did last night by threatening her, you will be dealt with, do you understand?"

He just stared at me.

I continued, "If I hear that you have discussed what has happened with anyone then, believe you me, I will be holding you responsible for the leak."

I didn't wait for any response. I got up from the table and wished him, "Good Day."

Rosa by this time was standing at the hotel entrance, the police car had arrived and as we drove off to the police station I wondered, after questioning Jawad, what other evidence, if any, had been found?

The police Inspector greeted us politely as we arrived to the police station.

"Please, have a seat, ladies. May I offer you some tea?"

"No, thank you," we both replied simultaneously. "We just had breakfast at the hotel, but thank you kindly," I said, hoping we had escaped from the dreaded sweet, milk tea.

"Well ladies, let me update you on the latest events."

"Yes," I said, "have you any more incriminating evidence?"

"We received confirmation from the hospital and forensics that Miss Rosa had been sexually assaulted and we found Jawad's DNA to prove it. Mr Jawad will now be formally charged with the violent rape of Miss Rosa and be held in custody till his court appearance."

"This is great news," I said, quite relieved, as was Rosa, that there was enough evidence to hold him and hopefully bring him to trial. Now, here comes the tricky part, I thought to myself. I have to convince the Police Inspector to allow the trial to take place in Saudi Arabia.

"Inspector, I had a call from the highest authority in Saudi Arabia who have thanked you so very much for your kindness and sensitivity towards Rosa and indeed your professionalism in expediting the case. Their final request, as per Saudi Authorities is Sir, that I would be allowed, if at all possible, to take Rosa and Jawad back to Saudi Arabia for justice to be served in a Saudi court. If you agree, the formal papers will be faxed to you immediately from Saudi Arabia?"

The inspector looked so puzzled and perplexed by my request. "This is an unusual request, Madam, as he has committed the crime here."

"I totally understand that Sir but our priority is getting Rosa back home to a familiar environment and Jawad, as a Saudi, to be tried in a Saudi court of law. We have a 747 jet at Delhi airport departing tomorrow, back to Saudi Arabia."

The Inspector turned to Rosa, "And what is your decision, Miss Rosa?"

"I wish to return to Saudi Arabia Sir, with Miss Lesley," she said.

After much thought and collaboration the Inspector thankfully agreed. "Well Ladies, if that is your wish I will make the arrangements. Tomorrow afternoon is the next flight to Saudi Arabia is that right Miss Lesley?"

"Yes Inspector, it is."

"Then I will send all the paperwork and evidence pertaining to this case to my counterpart in Saudi Arabia. Tomorrow, we will escort Mr Jawad to the aircraft just before departure."

"Will he be cuffed?" I asked.

"Yes and we will escort him but only to the aircraft door entrance where we will then remove his handcuffs. Anything else you wish to discuss Miss Lesley?"

"Well actually Sir, I have one more request. As you no doubt already know, one of our aircrafts crashed last month here in Delhi and with so much media talk going on about Saudi Arabia at this present time, I would ask you to please keep this incident away from the media. As you can imagine, it will not do the company nor indeed the country any good with any more bad publicity."

"Yes I will see what I can do?"

"Thank you Sir, these events have reached the highest authorities and on my return to the Kingdom I will be telling them of all you have done to protect Saudi Arabia's reputation."

As Rosa and I left the police station and were driven back to the hotel, I felt a great sense of relief. All I had to do now was to update the Captain and the so called Country Manager of today's events and outcome. On arrival at the hotel, Rosa went to her room and I called the captain.

"I will come down right now Lesley and meet you in the lobby for a coffee."

"Thank you Captain, see you shortly."

In the lobby as I related the events to the Captain he seemed satisfied with the outcome, although not very happy about bringing Jawad back with us on the same flight.

"I really don't want him travelling with us Lesley."

"Captain this is a request from Saudi Arabia, tomorrow it is a full flight in the economy section but there are no passengers in first or business class. I will therefore seat Rosa in the first class section and Jawad in the business section. I will take full responsibility for them captain. I must get them back to the kingdom for justice to be seen."

"I am still not happy, Lesley, with the situation, but okay, we will have them both on board."

"Thank you Captain, by the way Sir, your flight engineer, Rashid, called Rosa trying to get her to change her statement, please ask him to keep away from Rosa for the rest of the trip."

"Absolutely Lesley, I will talk to him."

Last port of call for me was now the Country Manager's suite, where a group of Saudi males had gathered, including the engineer Rashid. As I entered the room you could have cut the atmosphere with a knife. Just at that moment the phone rang.

"It's for you Lesley," said the Country Manager, handing me the phone.

"Hello Lesley, it's Yaser how are you? What has happened?"

"As you requested Yaser, the police will send you all the papers and evidence pertaining to the case. Both Rosa and Jawad will be on the flight tomorrow and we have kept the case away from the media."

"Well done Lesley, your work is almost completed."

"Almost Sir?"

"Yes, we now need you to supervise the flight, replacing Jawad tomorrow and remember to keep as much information about these recent events away from the other crew members until you get back here."

"Understood Sir, see you when we get back."

I left the Country Manager, went straight to my room and had a relaxing shower before getting dressed for dinner. I so just need a wee bit of me time. The restaurant which I hadn't been in since dinner with the captain and crew three days ago was so welcoming. It was dusk, as the sun set, little candles flickered on every table while soft melodies played in the background. The waiter came and took my order. A medium rare steak fillet accompanied by a large glass of ruby red Merlot. Yes, I thought that should do the trick! I relaxed, sipping my Merlot, pondering over the last few days. Gosh I thought, wait till I get hold of my lovely boss Mr Awadi. This has been some rest. Not !! I need to be re-scheduled on another flight another route somewhere like the Maldives, with sun, crystal blue waters and music! Oh well, a girl can dream can't she?

The next day Rosa is seated in the first class, as Carmen makes her comfortable with pillows and blankets. The passengers start to board at the rear. After the passengers are boarded the police escort arrives with Jawad. This is the first time I have seen him since he knocked my door on the night of the alleged rape. I can only imagine what might have been if I had opened my door?

"Salaam Jawad, can you kindly take a seat in the business class?"

"Salaam he replied, looking quite dishevelled, as one might expect, as he proceeded to his assigned seating."

I went to the captain, "We are ready to close the doors sir, all passengers on board."

Within minutes we had armed our doors and thank goodness we are on our way. It was a smooth flight. Rosa slept most of the way and it wasn't until about one hour before landing that Jawad asked to talk to me.

"Salaam Lesley, thank you for covering this flight. I am sorry for everything that has happened."

"Please Jawad, I don't want to know. The events of these last few days has hurt so many people, and Inshalla God will show you the right path. I have to go now, Jawad, and prepare the crew for landing."

As the wheels touched down, landing in Saudi Arabia, I felt so relieved. The doors opened, passengers deplaned and there standing waiting was my good friend Gabrielle, hugging Rosa, telling her "You are safe now." She looked to me and with a faint smile whispered, "Well done girl." As she helped Rosa away she turned "Get a good rest tonight Lesley, and meet me for coffee in my office around 10.00 a.m. tomorrow morning for a debrief."

"Yes," I smiled. I still remembered the routine from the old days, "see you tomorrow, good night."

A short distance away I could see the VIP manager, Yaser, with the police and security, escorting Jawad away.

After going through customs, it was so comforting to see Papa driving the car to take me home.

"How are you, Mam Lesley?"

"I am fine Papa just another week at the office!"

That night I slept like a log. Next morning, as the sun rose I was up and about. A quick dip in the pool and then off to meet with Gabrielle to review the hellish events of the past week in Delhi.

"Rosa is still at the hospital for another check-up. She is feeling so very stressed after such a terrible ordeal. However, she says thank you Lesley, for looking after her and helping her to remain strong."

"What about Jawad? What's his status?"

"As far as I know he is being questioned by the Saudi authorities and the evidence from Delhi is being scrutinized."

"Goodness Gabrielle, I hope I did the right thing in bringing him back and he isn't allowed to twist anyone round his finger?"

"Don't you worry," said Gabrielle, "they will throw his ass in jail."

"Now Lesley, as you can imagine, this is a high powered case so please make sure as you write your report you put the dot between the eyes. The case has reached the palace and you will be called and questioned by the King's legal team at some point in the near future."

I started to fill in the detailed report of the past five days' events and by the end of the day the report was ready. Gabrielle carefully read the report and looking up at me she said, "My Goodness, Lesley, I think one can only draw one conclusion from this report, and when the Saudi authorities acknowledge it, justice will be served and I wouldn't like to be in Jawad's shoes."

The next day I went back to my office in the training centre.

"What an ordeal Lesley, you handled it well, every step of the way."

"Yes Mr Awadi and you owe me one."

"What's that Lesley?"

"A flight to a desert island, without any people."

He laughed!

As I went to my desk my colleagues came around me to show their concern. But, later that day a threatening letter addressed to me appeared on my desk. I showed it to my boss.

"This is no good Lesley; I am so very sorry. Shall I get security?"

"No it's okay, it will be one of his crony friends, you know what I mean, 'birds of a feather'?"

And who you might ask threatened me? ... We will never know!

Guilty or Not Guilty

A few days pass before I was asked to attend an inquiry by lawyers from the royal court. Gabrielle accompanied me that day. As we arrived at the prestigious building, we were immediately shown through to a room with a panel of three middle-aged men, seated behind a long, beautifully carved oak table. They were well dressed in their Saudi finery and spoke English eloquently.

"Good Morning ladies, thank you for being here today."

"Miss Lesley and Miss Gabrielle, as you know this is indeed a very serious affair."

We both gave a gentle nod in agreement.

"Miss Lesley, we have in front of us a written report of the events that allegedly took place while in Delhi, to which you have signed."

"Yes Sir," I replied.

"We have evidence from both the Delhi and Saudi police, as well, of course, from Miss Rosa and Mr Jawad. Is there anything else you would like to add, Miss Lesley?"

"No, Sir."

"If we were to ask you, Miss Lesley, do you think Mr Jawad was guilty or not guilty what would be your reply?"

I was quite taken aback by such a question. I took my time to answer, reminding myself that this is Saudi Arabia; a man's world and on trial was a man whose family had strong connections. Was it a trick question I thought, because the answer could have far reaching consequences for those involved. I am not stupid, and, although the panel seem genuine, I am not letting them blame me for delivery of a guilty verdict, to cover their male, chauvinistic egos.

"Sir," I answered, "it is not for me to decide. You have my report. In the report I have described in detail the bruises and cuts on Rosa, the clump of hair missing from her head as she was pulled along the corridor and forced back into his room, which I realised were the screams that had awoken me up that night. From the hospital results, you have his DNA as verified by the Indian police. So I think, Sir, that with all these facts and evidence it is for you to decide not me!"

"Thank you, Miss Lesley, for helping us with our inquiries. That will be all."

"Thank you gentlemen," I replied, as Gabrielle and I stood up to leave.

As the driver took us back to Gabrielle's office she smiled.

"Well done Lesley, you held your ground."

"Well Gabrielle, it takes me back, having had you as a boss, I was taught by the best. In the whole scheme of things Gabrielle, it's not about us, it's about human rights and the truth, versus those with power, because of money and clout!"

"You are so right," she smiled.

A week or so later Jawad was found guilty of raping Miss Rosa. He was sentenced to lashing and prison.

Miss Rosa made a gradual recovery, but decided to go back home to her family in Syria!

It is not the oath that makes us believe the man, but the man the oath.

Aeschylus (525 – 456 BC)

Cabin Safety Inspector - London trip

*Shirome my maid
with Suki*

*My office in the
women's compound*

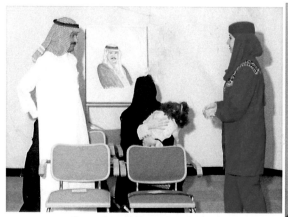

I am the veiled woman teaching
foreigners Saudi Culture

Meeting HRH in my Paris office

Met by jubilant crowds as we
arrive in Riyadh from Seattle
with first ever 747 glass cockpit

طيار سعودي يهنئ راكبة وصلت أمس إلى الرياض على متن الطائرة
الجديدة.

In my position
as Top Gun

PART 2

Spider's Web

Note to Reader:
The following chapters will demonstrate to you how, unknowingly, I have entered a spider's web built of lies, deceit, abuse, theft and fraud. This cleverly camouflaged web created so much misery. Through it I would have to fight for my life!

Fairy Tale

It's a lovely ten-minute walk from my apartment to the café, walking through well-tended, lush, green gardens with palm trees and desert flowers of many colours and scents. I am looking forward to meeting up with Emil. I haven't known her very long but she seems nice. She is from France and ever so chic with her elegant hair style and stylish wardrobe. She is married to one of the pilots in the company and has spent a number of years living in Saudi Arabia, although their actual home is one of the southern states in America. She has told me that she is a millionairess from her first marriage and her mansion sounds so appealing and quaint, kept cool in the Southern heat with traditionally-fashioned oak-bladed fans venting cool air around huge and well-appointed rooms. I think she has a most attractive lifestyle, as she tells me about her magnificent home. Her words conjure up images of a more ruthless, bygone age; owners of plantations sitting on their porches while African slaves worked endlessly on the land. Now, South Carolina can be proud of its mannerly people, well preserved architecture, distinguished cuisine and, of course, as the home of jazz. I think it sounds like paradise.

I feel at ease as I walk in to the quaint wee café with its décor of cool pastels, marble floors and soft music. This is where I regularly meet up with my girlie friends and have a good catch up. Emile, and I order two American coffees and the biggest, gooey, chocolate-iced donuts.

"So Lesley, have you met a nice man yet?"

"Not yet, Emile."

"It is time for you to meet someone nice and settle down. You are such a clever girl, good fun and kinda cute?"

"Kinda cute?" I said, as we laughed.

"You know Lesley, there are a lot of good men out there."

"I know Emile. I would love to find Mr Right and have a family, but you know how difficult it is to date in Saudi Arabia, so how will I find such a man?"

"Ah oui, that is true, but if I think of someone nice for you I will let you know."

"Ah oui," I replied, and again we laughed."

A few weeks later Emile called me.

"Bonjour Lesley, how are you, have you met Mr Right yet?"

"Gosh no Emile I have been so busy at work."

"Well, I know someone who wants to meet you. His name is Bassam. His family are friends of ours and we often go for breaks to their mansion in the Northern Region. What do you think Lesley?"

"Well, if you know him Emile, then that is a good start."

"Oh yes, Lesley, they are a respectable and prosperous family. Bassam himself is a successful business man with a mansion in Saudi Arabia and a second home in America; and guess what Lesley?"

"What?" I said.

"He has never been married."

"How old is he Emile?"

"I think around your age, Lesley."

Wow! I thought, this guy is ticking all the boxes.

"So what do you think Lesley? He wants to call you. Can I give him your number?"

"Yes," I replied, "why not?"

"Great! I am going to call him tonight, catch up soon."

"Okay Emile, bye."

As I put the phone down I felt quite excited, he sounded just perfect. Emile knew him, he was from an influential family and was a successful business man. After all it is every girl's dream to meet her knight in shining armour, isn't it?

That same night Bassam called me. We exchanged pleasantries and arranged

116

to meet the next day at a shopping mall. After the call, I spent so much time thinking about what to wear? In true honesty it probably wouldn't make such a difference as I would be covered with my veils. Finally, I decided to wear my pink lace Chanel blouse and contrasting long pencil style skirt. Of course my veils, which I have chosen to wear, are of pure silk, the latest design and so very chic.

The next day I got my driver to drop me at the entrance of the mall and within minutes a magnificent blue Mercedes drew up beside where I was standing. As the window went down the driver said:

"Hello Lesley, I am Bassam, the friend of Emile."

"Hello," I said, looking at him. He had a handsome face and kind smile.

He got out of the car and opened the passenger side door for me.

"May I invite you to go and have some tea at one of the cafe's Lesley?"

"That would be lovely," I said, as I sat in the luxurious leather seat.

He was tall, olive complexioned and looked quite muscular. I could feel my heart pounding as I thought, yes he is a bit of alright! We drove to a little café near the Cornish. It was a lovely afternoon as we chatted over a cup of Chi and Nana (mint tea).

"My family are from the Northern Region, Lesley. We look across the border to Aqaba in Jordan. It is one of the most beautiful spots on earth with its crystal blue waters, tropical fish of all colours shapes and sizes, and it is where our family yacht is anchored in the bay."

"It sounds so very beautiful, Bassam."

"It is," he said, "perhaps one day you can come and visit me there."

"Perhaps," I smiled.

"What about your family, Bassam, are they all living in the Northern Region?"

"Yes Lesley, most of us, although we do have properties and homes in other regions and other countries. I lost my father to cancer a few years ago. He was a Government Minister and I loved him so much. We tried every medication on the market to try and find a cure. We took him to America and every day my brother Talal and I would accompany him over the border to Mexico where there was an Oncology Centre with a miracle drug, but unfortunately it didn't work."

"I am so sorry."

"Thank you, Lesley. The royals were so kind and sent a private jet to bring my father's body back home to Saudi Arabia."

"He must have been well known?"

"Yes Lesley, he was respected by many and I loved him dearly. Whenever he held meetings with other ministers or dignitaries, I would sit amongst them, from when I was a small boy, listening to their talks and words of wisdom."

"What about your mum?"

"Her name is Leila, but unfortunately, she too doesn't keep so well."

"Who looks after her?"

"She lives in one of the mansions which I bought with my brother, Talal. We have a nursemaid who looks after her."

"Do you have many brother and sisters?"

"Yes, I do. I am especially close to Talal. He is the one who looks after the family business."

"Gosh, sorry Bassam, I hope I am not being too inquisitive?"

"Oh no, I am happy to share things with you about my family, I suppose this is part of a first date," he said, tongue and cheek.

"We were one of the first in Saudi Arabia to build water wells, that is how we made our money at the beginning and now we own many businesses such as dealing in precious gems, construction companies, wheat fields, olive groves and retail shops. In fact, in the Northern Region we own most of the lands the eye can see and beyond."

Gosh, I thought, it sounds as though they own the city; 'The Dallas Of Arabia'.

"What about you Lesley, Emile told me that you have a very high position in the airline and you have been with the company twenty-one years?"

"Oh yes Bassam I have a wonderful career and so enjoy my work."

"You look so young to have worked this long."

"Well, I will take that as a compliment."

"May I ask how old are you?"

"Yes, no problem, I am thirty-nine years old."

"Good age Lesley, I am in my thirties as well."

"Have you ever married?"

"No never, I just haven't had the time to meet someone special."

"Do you spend much time here in Saudi Arabia?"

"Yes, I fly back often to check on my lands and the business. But, I have to say that I find the restrictions here in Saudi Arabia just too much. It's like being in a gold fish bowl. Don't get me wrong, I love my country but I do not like to be dictated to by any government. I have a beautiful home in San Diego, with gardens, where I keep pink flamingos roaming freely on my land.

I actually graduated from the American University with my Doctorate in Psychology, but till now I have never actually practiced. I am lucky enough to have a good income from my lands and our family business here in the kingdom."

"Gosh Bassam, it seems you have been very lucky, as they say, born with a golden spoon."

"Oh Yes, I suppose you could say that. Money is of no object and now I feel it's the right time to find someone who could share this life with me."

I looked at him pensively, this seemed all too good to be true, but then a lot of this Emile had already told me. She knows him and his family, so it must be true. Gosh sometimes I wish I didn't analyse so much, but hey there you go, still in work mode.

"Why haven't you married a Saudi woman Bassam?"

"Oh no, I have no interest whatsoever in finding a wife from this country. They have such closed minds and become so fat as all they seem to do is spend their time eating and gossiping with the other women in the family."

"Sorry, but aren't you being a wee bit chauvinistic Bassam? In my opinion the women here don't have as many opportunities as we do in the Western world. But I am sure if they did and were so allowed, they would be driving themselves to work and having a career, earning their own money and if they could travel without needing a male member of the family's permission, I am sure the world would be their oyster."

"Well Lesley, you do have some views about my country."

"Indeed I do, Bassam. I love this country, but I am sorry to say, that a lot has to be done in the name of human rights especially with regards to women."

"You see Lesley, that's why I want to marry a foreigner. You are not scared to say what you believe. Like you, I know that we have to make a lot of changes, but this is so difficult as there is no freedom of expression. What about your family Lesley?"

"I visit my parents monthly in Scotland. I usually take a week off every month. We have a lovely villa there, which I own with my parents, like you with your father. I have the most beautiful, kind and wise mother."

"That's good Lesley, having a house gives you security for your future."

"Oh yes, and because of my position in the company I have an aviation pass that I will retire with, which allows me free and reduced tickets to travel the world, and discount in all major hotels. Actually as a tease I tell some of my male colleagues, marry me and fly free."

"Wow, Lesley, maybe I will take you up on that one day," we laughed.

"Would you like to marry at some point, Lesley?"

"Oh yes, if I meet Mr Right."

"What about a family?"

"Oh yes Bassam, that is my dream. One or two babies would be just perfect. Sorry I am becoming quite emotional."

In all honesty perhaps I was saying too much on a first date, but I felt so comfortable with him. He suddenly took my hand.

"Not at all Lesley, you seem like a girl after my own heart."

"Really?" I said, I could feel my face blush and my heart beat so much faster.

"Do you have any holidays coming up Lesley? What about next month, what are you doing for Christmas?"

"Well, normally I would be going home to spend the two weeks with my parents but I have a teaching trip to Indonesia in December and I am still waiting for the departure dates."

"I have never been to Asia Lesley. What's it like?"

"Well, I have to say that it is a beautiful continent of colour and contrasts. The people of Indonesia are a very humble people. I feel an air of serenity whenever I am there. I believe this is due to their culture and their belief in Buddhism, the way of life many of the people follow."

"Well, whenever you get your dates to depart to Indonesia, let me know and perhaps I will give you a surprise visit."

I smiled, "Sure, I will let you know," thinking, is this man for real?

"Lesley, do you know the base manager of Paris?"

"Oh yes, I know him well; Mr Hani. I did some work for him in Paris. He is a great guy and a brilliant boss."

"That's good to hear, you see he is my step brother."

"What?" said I, taken aback.

"Yes Lesley, he is older than me. His mother died during child birth and so my father remarried, to my mother Leila."

"My goodness 'what a small world'."

I looked at my watch; how time flies. "I think it is time for me to go home, but thank you for such a lovely afternoon. It has been great to meet you."

"Yes, it has for me also, I hope that I may invite you out again, only next time, dinner?"

"Yes, thank you, that would be great. I will look forward to it."

"Lesley if you wait here for a couple of minutes, I will get my car and bring it round to the front of the café."

"Thank you."

The Mercedes Benz stopped in front of the café and Bassam got out and opened the car door for me. What a gent, I thought! As he drove me home we continued chatting about what was happening in our lives.

"Your car is so very comfortable Bassam."

"Thank you, this is my new toy. The latest model, I just bought it yesterday.

Once you get to know me Lesley, you will find that I am quite a spontaneous person."

As we stopped in front of the apartments, I wished him "Good Night".

"And you too Lesley, I will call you soon."

As I entered my apartment, I felt as though I was floating on air, as though on a magic carpet. What a gorgeous guy. I wouldn't normally jump to such a conclusion so quickly but I feel so excited having been introduced to him. This could be the start of something special. After all, Emile knows him, he is my former Paris boss' step-brother, hailing from an affluent family, a successful business man in his own right and has never been married. What a reference!

I ask you – what is not to like? Is this a fairy tale? Has the princess met her prince?

During the next couple of weeks, I was wined and dined by Bassam. He took me to some renowned restaurants where often the powerful and influential dined, for example, one day the oil minister, Sheik Yamani, was sitting at the next table. My goodness now I am beginning to see how the other half live.

Two weeks later, the week of Christmas, Bassam and I were invited to Emile's house for drinks. It was there that I was introduced to his older brother, Talal.

"Hello Lesley and Bassam, welcome, please come in."

"Hi Emile," we said.

"Thank you for your invitation," as I handed her a beautiful Christmas bouquet, which I had specially ordered that morning from the famous flower shop near where I lived.

"Thank you Lesley, they are beautiful."

"You are so welcome Emile, Merry Christmas."

"Lesley let me introduce you to Talal."

"Good Evening Lesley, I am Talal."

"Good Evening Talal, nice to meet you."

"Isn't Lesley so pretty Talal", said Emile, "Bassam is such a lucky man."

"I felt a tad embarrassed and just tried to brush off what she said with a smile."

Talal said nothing.

"Lesley and Bassam, would you care for a drink?" asked Emile.

"Oh Yes, whatever you and Talal are having," we said, "that would be lovely."

"Okay, two gin and tonics coming up."

It was a pleasant enough evening although I felt a bit of a chill in the air. I am not sure about Talal, perhaps he is not too keen on me. I am really not sure; I mean he hardly knows me. I suppose only time will tell. A few more cooling gin and tonics and then it was time to take my leave.

"Thank you for the pleasant evening, Emile."

"It is still early Lesley?"

"I would have enjoyed staying a bit longer, but I really do have an early start in the morning."

Talal stood up, "Nice to have met you Lesley."

"It was lovely to have met you also, Talal. Enjoy the rest of your evening."

As Bassam drove me home he said something rather strange, which I have never forgotten.

"Please Lesley, be careful around Emile."

"What do you mean?"

"Well I know she has introduced us to each other, which is great, but beware of her, because as both Talal and I know, she is very materialistic, a terrible gossip and will betray those close to her for the highest bidder. Money is her God."

"Oh Bassam, she has been a good friend till now, aren't you being a tad unfair?"

"All I am saying Lesley, is watch what you say. Talal has known her and her daughter for many years, believe me, she has the gift of turning the truth around. I am only telling you this Lesley for your own sake!"

When I got home I felt a little unsettled about the conversation. I said nothing to him at this point, but some colleagues and close friends of mine had said the very same thing about her previously. The thing is, since I met her she has been just lovely and I have never had a reason to think otherwise. I do believe, as I am sure you will have surmised by now, that everyone deserves a chance until proven otherwise. I suppose only time will tell?

Asian Adventure

Bassam has gone to Paris during the Christmas festivities, to visit his brother Hani. It's the 27th of December and I am on my way to Jakarta, the capital of Indonesia, for two weeks, to conduct the training of new stewardesses. I have been here so many times and can vouch that it is indeed a country of serenity. One always feel alive and at peace with oneself when here. The classes are always enjoyable as the trainees are ever so gracious and humble. The majority of people are Muslim while the other recognised religions are Christianity, Hinduism and Buddhism. Such wonderful diversity. Jakarta is a shopping hub with numerous malls and traditional markets. The food, as you might imagine is absolutely delicious, varies according to the regions and could be of Chinese, Indian, middle Eastern and even European roots. So, as usual, lucky me – between trainings I will be shopping, sampling local delicacies and in this tropical climate relaxing by the pool in the grounds of this magnificent hotel.

I have to say that at some point I would love to visit the Island of Bali. I have heard it is so very beautiful, with never ending sun-soaked beaches, a lush barrier reef, temples where the locals hold colourful and beautiful rituals. A sanctuary, a place to relax, meditate and be at one with nature. Yes, definitely my kind of place!

Training has started and as I surmised my class of trainee stewardesses are just lovely. It is now evening and I am relaxing in my hotel suite with a glass of wine, chatting with one of my Egyptian colleagues, Sophia.

"So Lesley, how is it going with this guy that you met, sorry what's his name?"

"His name is Bassam. He seems nice Sophia. We have been out a few times for dinner, caught up with friends and I have already met up with one of his brothers, Talal."

"So, is it serious then?"

"Too early to tell," I said, "but so far so good."

"When are you planning to meet up with him again?"

"Not sure, Sophia, but can you believe it, he said that he might come to see me here in Indonesia."

"Gosh Lesley, he must be keen. He has only known you a month and already he's talking about travelling to another continent, just to see you?"

"I know Sophia. I mean how many guys would fly ten hours to another country to meet up with someone they had just met?"

Just then there was a knock at the hotel door.

"Oh," said Sophia jokingly, "that must be him?"

I opened the door, it was one of the bell boys.

"Good Evening Miss Lesley, this telegram is for you."

"Thank you," I said, as I took the telegram and closed the door.

"What does it say?" asked Sophia.

"My goodness, it's from Bassam, he says that he will be arriving here on New Year's Eve and that he loves me."

"What?" said Sophia, totally bewildered.

"Gosh, that is the day after tomorrow!"

"Wow Lesley, this guy is keen, you lucky woman."

Sure enough on the 31st December, just as the sun was setting, Bassam's aircraft touched down in Indonesia. I took the hotel's chauffeur-driven limousine to go and meet him at the airport. He was the last to come through customs, having stopped in the Duty Free, and now appeared, laden with lots of goodies: bottles of champagne, the finest wines and lots of chocolates.

I was happy to see him, although rather surprised that he was still in Saudi dress?

"Hi Lesley," he said, giving me the biggest hug ever.

"Hi Bassam, I am so glad you are here. Did you have a good flight?"

"Yes, very relaxing. Excuse me, still being in my Saudi robes but I came straight from our office and didn't have time to change."

"You must have been so busy in the office?"

"We are making lots of business deals Lesley but I just didn't want to miss the flight and not see you."

Gosh, I thought, this guy is a real go getter. A true example of the word entrepreneur, but still finding time to travel to another continent for little me. At last, I feel special!

On reaching the hotel, Bassam checked into his room and we met later in the lobby just before midnight, bringing in the New Year of 2000 together. We had a great time. The champagne flowed as we mixed with other revellers, hugging and dancing amidst streamers and balloons in the hotel lobby.

"What's your New Year resolution, Bassam?"

"To catch you," he laughed.

"Oh well," I said with a mischievous smile, "all good things are worth waiting for."

Around 2.00 a.m., after a few more glasses of bubbly, we retired to our rooms.

"I will meet you in the lobby tomorrow, when you finish work, Lesley."

"Great, Bassam, I should be back around 5.00 p.m. What are you going to do today?"

"I will probably relax at the pool, swim a few lengths, then perhaps do some sightseeing."

"Great idea," I said, "enjoy yourself."

I couldn't wait to finish my class and get back to the hotel to see Bassam. Sure enough, he was sitting waiting for me in the hotel lobby.

"Hi Lesley," he said, hugging me ever so tightly.

"Hello Bassam, did you have a good day?"

"Yes I did. I had a swim and then went outside and took a little tour around the city. I was thinking Lesley, how about we have dinner here in the hotel? They have an excellent Chinese restaurant."

"A great idea, in fact I had dinner there the other night. They prepare the loveliest dim sum and delicious Peking duck with pancakes."

"Okay Lesley, let's go there. You must be tired after being on your feet all day. Would you like to rest?"

"No, I will just go have a shower and freshen up."

"Okay, I will walk you to your room."

I opened the door of my room and my goodness what had happened. I thought I was in the honeymoon suite, it looked so different. Bassam smiled.

"Did you do this?" I asked excitedly.

"Yes I did," he replied.

My suite was filled with hundreds of beautiful colourful orchids. On my bed there were lots of beautifully wrapped gifts, in boxes with giant bows.

"What's this?" I said, as though I had been handed the moon.

"It's all for you Lesley, I am sorry it is a bit delayed but, Merry Christmas!"

"You didn't have to do this," I said.

"Oh yes I did," he smiled.

"Thank you so much, Bassam. No one has ever done anything like this for me before."

There was a bottle of champagne on ice, and as Bassam poured I started to open my gifts. The most expensive perfumes and a variety of silk dresses, all flown from Paris.

"Oh Bassam, this is too much. You really didn't have to do this."

"To our future Lesley," he smiled, handling me a glass of champagne.

That night, over dim sum, we chatted about our lives and what we wanted to do in the future

"I am a champion clay pigeon shooter Lesley, perhaps one day we can travel to Egypt and I will take you to my private club."

"That would be nice. I have never been to a shoot before. As long as it is just clays and not a real animal hunt, that is fine with me."

"Would you not go on real hunt Lesley?"

"Absolutely not Bassam, I think it's very cruel, killing for sport, just to satisfy a man's ego."

"Well, don't worry, it is only clays. I would never shoot an animal for sport. By the way Lesley, I am going to Brunei for some family business. I am hoping to meet up with his Majesty the Sultan of Brunei. Why don't you join me there when you finish the training?"

"Oh my, isn't the Sultan of Brunei one of the world's wealthiest individuals?"

"Yes, his peak worth is around $20 billion dollars."

"Oh my goodness, one person having so much. I bet you he has some palace? Would I need a visa?"

"I don't think, being British, you would need one, but if so I can take care of that at the airport when you arrive."

"Are you sure you can arrange this? It wouldn't be much fun being deported back."

"Don't worry, you are in safe hands."

Note to Reader:

Honestly, at this point in time, I really did think I had met Prince Charming; a real gent, someone I could rely on, who just didn't talk the talk but also walked the walk.

Bassam left for Brunei, calling me every day about the beautiful country and how well his business meetings were going. I decided to join him there at the end of my working assignment.

"That's great Lesley, that you are joining me here. Its just like paradise. Keep your hotel suite open in Jakarata, perhaps you might decide to spend some more time there when you return back from Brunei."

"Gosh Bassam sorry, but keeping this suite open for a week will cost a lot of money."

"You do have crew discount in hotels don't you?"

"Yes I do Bassam, but still, unlike you, I am not a millionaire."

"Well, no problem," he said, "I will take care of it."

"Are you sure Bassam? Paying for a hotel suite that I will not be in seems such a waste of money."

"Lesley, I am very spontaneous and this is the lifestyle I live, so you better get used to it."

"Okay."

"Just get you ticket and I will see you here tomorrow."

As I came off the phone, I thought well this must be how the other half live. Okay, I haven't known Bassam very long and it's not his fault that he is born with a golden spoon. I am not a hypocrite, I suppose not to have to worry about money, be able to do and buy anything you want at any time must of course be wonderful, but everything in life comes at a cost. Yes, I am having such fun and enjoying his company but I feel a tad embarrassed at the amount of money he seems to go through. It's not that I am jealous or trying to dampen this moment in time but when I think of the child Mestizo and all the other babies around the world who have to beg for a piece of bread, it makes me very uncomfortable, or perhaps I am being unfair. There I go again, analysing the facts. I must stop this and leave my work behind otherwise I might never meet Mr Right and settle down? I must give myself a shake and stop being so fussy, relax and enjoy the moment, this wonderful wee adventure in Paradise with a cool guy that I really quite like.

I bought a ticket to Brunei and by the end of the week, I too was on my way.

Paradise

It was an enjoyable two hour, thirty minute flight to Brunei with blue skies and not a cloud to be seen.

I was still a little nervous about having no visa, entering an Islamic country. I worried about the rules for a single woman. Well I needn't have bothered; as I walked to passport control an airport official approached me

"Miss Lesley?"

"Yes," I said, rather nervously.

"Please come this way, Mr Bassam is waiting for you."

I followed the official as he led me through the airport, bypassing the passport control and customs. Outside in the beautiful sunshine Bassam was waiting in the embassy car.

"Welcome to Brunei, Lesley."

The chauffeur opened the car door for me, as my luggage was promptly put in the boot. Sitting in the luxurious BMW I felt as though I was on cloud nine as we drove through the beautiful city to the First Class luxury hotel.

"Lesley, I hope you don't mind, I bought this gift for you?"

"Thank you so much," I said, as I opened the carefully wrapped package containing a beautiful Christian Dior, multi-coloured, silk scarf.

"Lesley, whenever we go out of the hotel, would you mind wearing this scarf as it is part of the protocol here?"

"Of course Bassam, that will be fine. You know I am already used to the veil and this scarf is ever so beautiful. So I suppose I will not be able to sunbathe in my bikini?" I said mischievously.

"Oh absolutely, you will. Wait until you see the hotel's pool and magnificent beach. While you are in the vicinity of the hotel and grounds you are free to dress as you like. It's just when you leave the hotel we should follow the tradition of the people here."

The hotel was absolutely magnificent, like living in a palace, with its great and spacious rooms, satin sheets and duvets of feather down. The opulent dining room was hung with chandeliers and its tables well presented with solid silver cutlery and crystal vases of bright yellow flowers called Simpor. When in full bloom, they looked like little yellow umbrellas. (Native flower of Brunei). The people are so warm, humble and friendly. The women, wearing colourful, traditional dress, worn so simply but with so much finesse. I feel utterly pampered and so relaxed amongst this carefree people. Perhaps this is due to the Bruneian combination of Malay traditions as its cultural root, with Islam at its heart. Perhaps this is also the reason for such mutual respect between their monarch and his people.

During the day while, Bassam attends business meetings, I happily relax on the hotel's man-made beach which is absolutely spectacular, with the most crystal blue waters I have ever seen. In the evening we dine in beautiful restaurants and take walks amongst the majestic gardens.

"So Lesley, can you believe it, one week is gone and tomorrow we return to Jakarta. Did you enjoy your time?"

"Very much Bassam, it was just lovely."

"What about you? Did your business meetings go as well as you thought they would?"

"Oh yes, brilliantly."

"Would you ever contemplate living here Lesley?"

"Oh yes, at the drop of a hat."

"That's good, me too, who knows what the future will bring?"

I felt my heart flutter. Was he talking about us, together living here in Paradise? Next day, we boarded our flight, returning back to Jackarta, to continue on this wonderful wee adventure.

Island of The Gods

The following morning, back in Jackarta I am on my hotel balcony, relaxing over a buffet breakfast of fresh papaya with squeezed lemon, freshly prepared orange juice, selection of warmed pastries, croissants and coffee. The view is stunning, the calmness of a vast Indonesian ocean and skyline so very blue. The early morning sun rises as I am kept cool by a gentle breeze.

When we arrived back from Brunei it was late evening so I am sure Bassam is still snuggling under his duvet. I notice that he is not really an early bird, even his business meetings seem to be arranged late afternoons or sometimes evening. Unlike me, I so enjoy the mornings, I think it's the best time to gather your thoughts and plan your day.

"Good Morning, Lesley,"

"Good Morning, Bassam," I said, as he joined me on the balcony. "Did you sleep well?"

"Yes thank you, I made a few business calls to my brother, Talal and other associates. By the way, Talal is saying 'Hello,' to you."

"Really?" I said, "so you told him we were meeting here?"

"Oh yes Lesley, and I am so looking forward to you meeting the rest of my family."

"Thank you, that would be nice."

As he sat down, he looked ever so handsome in his yellow polo shirt and shorts. The diamonds on his gold Rolex watch sparkled as they hit the glare of the midday sun.

"Look at your watch Bassam sparkling in the sunshine."

"Oh yes Lesley, look at yours too."

Sure enough my gold Rolex with its emerald face and diamonds, was also sparkling in the sun. I loved my little watch, which I had bought second hand. It looked brand new, as it had never been worn by its previous owner. It took me three months to be able to afford it. I never have it off my wrist, unless I am going to any special events, to which, I would probably wear my diamond Chopard, which you will remember was a gift given to me by the now King Fahad Al Saud of Saudi Arabia.

"Lesley, you are away in a dream?"

"Sorry Bassam, I was just lost in thought."

"Well, I was thinking," he said, "I remember you mentioned to me that you would someday like to visit the Island of Bali. What about if we go there now?"

"What do you mean by, now?" I asked, sitting upright on my chair.

"Well, there are flights all day to the island, so if we go down town now to the travel office we could catch a late afternoon flight?"

"I have just unpacked, can't we go tomorrow and catch an early flight so we can enjoy the full day on the island?"

"Come on Lesley, I told you that I am spontaneous. I really do like you and I think you are the one," he said with a mischievous smile, "You really must try and keep up with me."

I ignored the remark that 'I was the one,' but I could see how upbeat he was and raring to go. I really didn't want to dampen the mood.

"Okay Bassam, let's go."

It's now late afternoon and we have been in the downtown ticket office for about two hours. Yes, you heard me right. For the last two hours Bassam has been bartering non-stop and haggling for the best offer, to try and get the least expensive four-day package to the island. Okay, perhaps this is a good sign that he is not as I thought, always throwing money away, but this is too much, even the ticket agent I believe is struggling not to put his head in the oven or perhaps just jump from his office window, for a quick getaway.

Gosh, I thought, it really isn't an expensive trip, so what's is going on?

"Bassam, I can buy my own ticket if you like?"

"No Lesley, I am dealing with this".

Another hour passes and at last we have our tickets for our trip to Bali.

A quick dash back to the hotel, get packed and we catch the last flight to the Island.

The flight time to the Island is about two hours, so by the time we arrive it's already ten o'clock in the evening. We are driven to our hotel, which is very traditional and looks so very lovely with its thatched roof and wooden lobby, depicting many hand-carved wooden sculptures and Batik prints. The end of the lobby leads you to the most beautiful gardens, with tropical, lush blossoms surrounding a deep pool made out of rocks, gently caressed by a nearby waterfall. What one might call a wee haven. We checked into our rooms which have balconies overlooking the pool and gardens. All is ever so quiet except for soft Balinese sounds of music in the background, quiet conversation of other guests and the ripples of the pool.

We have decided, as this is our first evening on the Island, to explore the nearby surroundings of our hotel. We come across a quaint restaurant, from the outside looking quite native with its thatched roof and wooden exterior, while inside so very welcoming with a relaxing ambience, created by low, wooden, carved tables with long burning candles, giving off a gentle glow around. We sat there on big comfy cushions. It was here that Bassam introduced me to the native Japanese dish of sushi, which to this day, is one of my favourite dishes of the Orient. It was such a wonderful and romantic setting.

"Can you believe it Lesley, we have known each other only three months and have already travelled together to three countries, covering two continents?"

"Yes I know; I think it is what people might call a 'whirlwind romance'."

"I like that thought, Lesley."

"Me too," I replied.

Next day, I rose early. On opening my balcony shutters I was so happy to see, yet again, the sunshine and tropical gardens, with almost every type of flower one could imagine, a rainbow of vibrant colours and scents spreads across this Island of the Gods. As Ralph Waldo Emerson once said about Bali, 'the earth laughs in flowers.'

Sun worshippers are already relaxing by the pool and lapping up the luxury of being served by friendly waiters, in traditional costumes of sarong. Bassam hasn't called, he must still be asleep, or perhaps making business calls, so I will go ahead and have my breakfast beside the pool. It's 10.00 a.m. and still no sign of Bassam. I think I will just go for a dip in the hotel pool.

"Good Morning, Madam. Would you like me to prepare one of the sun beds for you to relax?"

"Yes thank you, but please in a little bit of shaded area."

"Of course, Madam."

I soon drifted off listening to my CD, with the latest collection of soul music.

"Hello Lesley, are you awake?"

"Yes, Bassam, gosh I must have dozed off. Did you have a good sleep?"

"Yes thank you, but as usual, I had some business calls to make. I am now ready to relax beside you. Shall we take a dip?"

"Yes," I said, as he took my hand and led me to the pool. The water was so cooling as we slowly waded in, then gently swam around the façade of little rocks and foliage, reaching the waterfall where we just lay back and relaxed.

"After lunch Lesley, would you like to have a walk and explore our surroundings?"

"Yes absolutely Bassam and perhaps we could go on some tours, if you are not too busy with business?"

"Sounds a good idea. After we get back from our walk, why don't you go to the tour office in the hotel and choose some trips for us to go on. I need to close up some business deals in the meantime."

I thought, isn't he lovely, so caring and yet seems ever so astute at business. So able to multi-task, keeping his eye on the family empire while, at the same time, making sure I that I am okay and enjoying my holiday. After a delicious seafood lunch by the pool, followed by an afternoon walk round the local shops, Bassam retires to his room to deal with business, while I go and book some of the Islands tours. I spent some time with the tour representative as there are so many wonderful things to see and do on the Island.

"Thank you," I said, choosing three of the trips which I thought both Bassam and I would enjoy.

"Could you please do a tentative booking on all three tours for me and I will confirm with you later this afternoon?"

"Absolutely Madam, which trips would you be interested in?"

"Well they all sound so wonderful; we are so spoiled for choice. So firstly, the day trip tomorrow to view the Royal temples and shrines before going on to the rainforest and visiting the monkey sanctuary please. Then the next day the island water adventure with the fly fishing, snorkelling and underwater scooter rides."

"Oh yes Madam, that is a fun day."

"Yes, I like to snorkel and I know my boyfriend enjoys fishing."

"Finally, for our last evening on the island, I think it would be nice for us to relax before our trip back to Jackarta?"

"Yes Madam, what about our Sunset tour to one of our beautiful white beaches, where you will be entertained by our Kecal mythological dancers while enjoying a delicious seafood barbecue with tropical cocktails?"

"Sounds ideal, thank you for your time. You really have been so helpful. I will confirm my bookings later in the evening."

"Thank you, Madam, enjoy the rest of your day."

Leaving the tour office, I saw Bassam coming out of the Ralph Lauren/Polo shop, in the hotel foyer.

"Hi, I have tentatively booked us some tours."

"Great Lesley, I have just been and bought myself some casual tops and shorts. What do you think?" he said, as he showed me his trendy new clothes.

"Wow," I said "you will be the trendiest guy on the island."

"Oh my goodness, Lesley, look at the time! We have to rush. Let's go and change quickly. We have ten minutes."

"Why Bassam? Where are we going?"

"It's a surprise."

"Well, shall I dress formal or casual."

"Oh, quickly, it doesn't really matter. One of your sun dresses will be fine."

Here we go again, I thought, Mr Spontaneous!

The hotel limousine sped away as Bassam told him that we only had a few minutes to spare before the boat sailed.

"We are going on a boat?" I asked him.

"Yes, it's a night cruise around the island."

I then asked the driver "How long will it take to get to the boat?"

"Fifteen minutes, Madam."

"Oh Bassam, it will have sailed, it's too late."

"It's never too late Lesley, I will place you a bet of ten dollars that we catch the boat."

"Okay, I hope so."

Arriving to the harbour the driver pointed to the open sea.

"Sir, I am sorry. Look the ship has sailed."

As we got out of the limousine, Bassam approached three Indonesian gentlemen, who appeared to be working on what looked like a large inflatable rubber dinghy. He conversed with them, pointing to the ship in the distance, gave them some money and then, low and behold, we are now in the rubber dinghy, in hot pursuit of the ship. As we got nearer to the ship, our three boatmen were shouting: "boat ahoy", "boat ahoy." I couldn't believe it, the ship started to slow and eventually stopped. As we approached, alongside the ship, one of its crewman pointed to a ladder. My goodness, I thought, are we meant to go up that. I felt so embarrassed as there were so many onlookers, both passengers and crew, waving and shouting "Come on, you can do it."

Talk about trying to arrive in style. I tell you it is no easy feat climbing a ladder with heals. It felt as though I was walking up the plank. What else could possibly happen? Perhaps we will be met by Captain Hook, because at this moment in time, I feel like I am on a date with Peter Pan.

"Good Evening," said one of the crew members, as we climbed on board.

"Mr Bassam, isn't it, we were hoping you would make it?"

"Good evening, Madam."

"Good evening," I said, trying to compose myself.

Just then, two stunningly beautiful Indonesian ladies approached us, putting a scented flower lei around our necks, followed closely by two of the stewards with canapés and very much appreciated cocktails. Eventually we started to relax and mingle with some of the other passengers. As we reached the open sea the colours of the sky changed to delightful shades of orange, purple and red.

Dinner was a scrumptious affair. We opted for the native cuisine, a variety of meat and fish dishes beautifully presented on banana leaves and coconut husks, watered down by the local rice wine, whilst in the background a trio were singing traditional Batak songs. People started dancing to live music, while I and Bassam opt to go to the upper deck where a starry sky awaits us. The ocean, the stars, the rice wine and music. Even our fragrant yellow and white leis, of frangipani, evoke a tropical feeling through their sweet scent and sheer beauty.

They say that frangipani denotes the femininity ruled by Venus; its element being water, its deity Buddha. They also say its power is love and its magical uses are in love spells. Without sounding too cheesy, maybe its magic is working on me.

Well it's the end of my adventure on The Island of the Gods. Tomorrow, early morning, I will catch a flight back to the mainland and from there back home to Saudi Arabia. Bassam is not travelling with me. He told me last night that he will stay on in the island, as he has arranged to meet up with some local business men.

Do you see what I mean, Mr Spontaneous?

***

A few months pass, I am busily working back in Jeddah while Bassam has been spending some weeks with the family business in Cairo. He calls me regularly, updating me on what's happening.

"The businesses and properties are doing well here in Cairo Lesley, and in between I am enjoying my clay pigeon shoots at the range. Do you have any days off this month?"

"Yes I do, Bassam, why?"

"Well in two weeks' time I am travelling to the beach resort of Hurghada along the Egyptian red coast. It is about a one hour and thirty minutes' plane ride from Jeddah. Have you ever been?"

"No, but I heard it's a fabulous place to holiday and enjoy oneself. Isn't Hurghada near Luxor, Valley of the Kings?"

"It certainly is. In fact, I was thinking, if you have nothing planned, why don't you join me there and together we could do a day trip to Luxor and explore The Valley of the Kings?"

"Well, I was planning to go to Scotland, but a trip to Hurghada sounds wonderful. I can delay my trip to Scotland till next month."

"Super Lesley, remember to pack your swimwear as the snorkelling is awesome."

"I am packing as we speak Bassam, see you in two weeks' time."

Two weeks later I am in Hurghada with Bassam. We are staying in a chic apartment with breathtaking sea views. By day, we spend time on the beach, snorkelling in what only can be described as a coral wonderland. Corals of so many shapes and colours, are the playgrounds of the many species of marine life: turtles, giant squid, and fish of orange, yellow, blue, green spots and stripes. Dive a bit deeper and playful dolphins become your best friend. In the evening we take walks along the main street which becomes like that of Aladdin's time. The whole of the street is lined with tall, flaming torches, chests of jewels with gold coins, and belly dancers showing intricate moves to the sounds of traditional Arabic beats, which come to life through guitar, drums and violin.

This evening, Bassam has told me that his friend, the Mayor of Hurghada, has given us his luxury yacht, with crew on board, for a night sail along the bay. It was one of the most magical times I have ever had. The yacht was indeed luxurious, with private rooms and kitchens and ten crew members on board to look after our every whim. Bassam's cousin, Mourad and his friend joined us on the night sail. As we dropped anchor an hour's sail from Hurghada, the crew, believe it or not, started to fish for our dinner. The only tool used was a long piece of string with a hook at the end. It is so wonderful to watch and I am so very proud of Bassam who has caught the first fish. After the seafood banquet we relax on deck. The only sounds audible are the gentle ripples on the water and distant voices from another boat getting ready for their night dive. The lull of the sea and soft Arabian melodies would eventually rock us to sleep under the canopy of a vast Arabian sky. What a life!

This is our last day in Hurghada. We have decided that for our last night we will relax and visit one of our favourite restaurants and sample some traditional Egyptian fayre.

"Have you enjoyed your time Lesley?"

"Oh yes, yet again, it has been wonderful. You really do know how to enjoy your life."

"Well yes, I believe life is for living and I have the money to do it."

"Yes, you are lucky, but I need to say something."

"What's that, Lesley?"

"Just something I need to make clear."

"Yes, go on."

"Well you do talk about money a lot. I need you to understand something that's important to me."

"What's that, Lesley?"

"Well I am not dating you because of your money. Okay, I am not born with a golden spoon like you, but I have worked very hard to be where I am and yes, I am not a millionaire but I do have a wonderful life. Like you, I have travelled the world and seen so many wonderful things. You really don't have to try and impress me."

"Oh please Lesley, I didn't mean anything untoward, I know you are a very successful woman in your own right."

"Yes Bassam, I just needed to clarify this point with you. If I wanted to marry for money, then I wouldn't have waited this long. I feel quite at ease and so enjoy your company, although our lives till now have really been quite different."

"Yes Lesley, but we are learning from each other and that's what I hope we will continue to do."

Bassam took my hand. "I think this is why it's working Lesley, sorry but I think we are just perfect for each other."

Just then the waiter arrived with an array of dishes. We sampled and enjoyed them all, followed by a refreshing dessert of Pistachio ice cream.

"Lesley, I am sorry that I am always on the phone but you see, I am in the stock market and have indeed made a lot of money from it."

"Really?" I said, "Sorry, but I really don't know too much about the stock market. Isn't it a bit like gambling?"

"Oh not at all, Lesley, I am not a gambling man."

"Sorry, I didn't mean anything by that remark Bassam, it's just you hear so many stories of people who are very successful and then throw it all away by taking too many risks?"

"Not me Lesley, I invest for my brother, Talal, and many of my friends. They trust me because of my knowledge and expertise in this area and I have never let any of them down. I never take risks, especially with other people's money. I am very astute regarding the stock market. This is another reason why I am able to travel and enjoy life the way I do."

"You make it sound so easy and simple, Bassam."

"Would you like me to invest for you? I promise I will double your money in three months' time?"

"I only have some savings in the bank, but it is for my future."

"Lesley, I was hoping I would be your future? Look if I invest for you I promise it will be without any risk. If something unforeseen was to happen, which never has, I will give you back your money from my account. So, you have a win-win situation Lesley."

"I don't have much money with me, Bassam."

"Don't you have a visa card?"

"Yes I do, a Gold Visa, but I never use it. I keep it for emergency use only.

I would rather take time to think about this, go back to Jeddah and go over my account with my bank manager Mr Hussein."

"Lesley, after everything I have said, don't you trust me?"

I was now feeling guilty, he has been so kind to me, perhaps I am being a tad unfair and selfish?

"Lesley, I am sorry, I don't want to appear to be pushy. I am coming to Jeddah next week, so you have a think and we can do it then. Shall I get the bill and then we could go for a stroll?"

"Yes Bassam, that would be lovely."

That night we walked for the last time on the sands of Hurghada.

"I love you, Lesley, I want to look after you and protect you forever, you must learn to trust me and know I would never hurt you!"

The following day, I left to go back to Jeddah as Bassam travelled back to Cairo. After arriving in Jeddah, I called my Bank Manager.

"Good Morning, Mr Hussein, it is Lesley from Saudia. I thought I should call you to arrange an appointment to see you in the bank. How are you?"

"I am great, thank you Lesley, haven't seen you for a couple of weeks."

"Yes, I have been quite busy with work and yesterday I arrived back from a break in Hurghada. Is it possible to pop into the bank this afternoon, before Maghrib (sunset prayer)."

"Of course Lesley, is everything alright?"

"Yes, I just need a little advice regarding my savings?"

"Sure Lesley, I look forward to seeing you."

It's late afternoon as I relax in the limousine, while the driver takes me to the souq for my appointment with Hussein at the Arab Bank. This time of day is just perfect for venturing into the souq, as the heat of the day is replaced by a cooling breeze, amidst a stunning sunset with its myriad of colours reds, orange and yellows in this wonderful land.

"Salaam Alaykum, Hussein."

"Alaykum Salaam, Lesley, please have a seat. Would you care for a Turkish coffee?"

"Yes, thank you. Goodness, I wish all our bank managers were like you back home."

"Thank you, so tell me, how can I help you?"

"Well, I have met someone special who I have been dating now for about six months. He is Saudi and from a good family."

"Is he living here?"

"Well, he is originally from the Northern Region, has a house in America and conducts the family business in the Middle East and in America, so he travels a lot. He also speculates in the stock market and the other day he offered to invest money for me."

"Lesley, I don't need to know your private affairs, but please be careful. You have saved over twenty years with us, I really don't advise you to take any risks."

"He is a good man Hussein. Remember when I worked in the office in Paris, well that was with his brother, Hani."

"Even so Lesley, you must be careful, the stock market is still a bit of a gamble."

"He said he will give me back my money in three months and if shares, for any reason, plummeted, he would reimburse me."

"I think you have made your mind up Lesley. How much do you want to invest?"

"Not a big amount Hussein, around 10,000 Saudi Riyals (approx £2,000 sterling). I mean it would be rather nice to have that doubled in three months."

"Lesley, it's your money, but please, be careful."

"Thank you, I will."

The following week Bassam arrived back in Jeddah. He picked me up and drove to one of our favourite Arabian restaurants. As I entered the car, I handed him the money in an envelope.

"Bassam this is my 10,000 riyals for investing."

He took the envelope without saying very much, if anything at all.

"So Bassam, can you please remember to return my investment by October?

Sorry to go on about it, I know it's not much to you, but receiving double the money back will be great and I can surprise mum with a beautiful gift."

"Of course I will, remember you are with a winner and the winner takes it all!"

Through dinner he seemed a bit preoccupied.

"I have to leave tomorrow, back to Egypt, Lesley."

"So soon, you just got here?"

"I know, but I have important business to deal with. However, on a lighter note, I was thinking of joining you in Scotland and meeting your parents. What do you think?"

"Well yes, Bassam, I am sure they would very much like to meet you."

"That settles it then, I will fly from Cairo at the end of the month and meet you there. You can show me round your beautiful country."

"Sounds wonderful and as it's still summer, hopefully, we will have a few good days of sunshine left to enjoy."

I arrived home to Scotland ahead of Bassam and it was so lovely to be with mum and dad again. Bassam is arriving in two days' time and I know mum is so looking forward to meeting him. She already met his brother, Hani, ten years ago when she came to visit me with my beautiful Aunt Helen (mum's best friend).

"I am so looking forward to meeting him, Lesley, is he as handsome as his brother Hani?"

"I think he is really quite cool. He seems so focused on being successful in the family business and like me he wants to have a family. I just feel it's the right time Mum!"

"Has he asked you to marry?"

"Not exactly, well we have only been dating nine months, but who knows?"

"As long as he is kind to you Lesley, that's what matters."

"You are right mum. Like me, he loves his parents and he is so looking forward to meeting you. He even said he would like to look at some properties while he is here. Wouldn't that be amazing mum, winter in Saudi

Arabia and summer in Scotland. You and dad would enjoy coming over to Saudi for vacations wouldn't you?"

"Oh yes, Lesley, we so enjoyed our last visit. I will always remember the kindness of the people, the colours and smells of spices in the Souq, and the feeling of calmness and contentment as I took my first steps into the warm waters of the red sea. What a wonderful trip that was."

Two days later Bassam arrived. Dad and I went to greet him at the historic Sherwood Castle hotel, where I had booked a room for him. I had paid in advance; my way of saying, welcome to my home. As usual, Bassam was late coming from his room.

"Hello Alexander," he said, to my father, "sorry for keeping you waiting. I had a lot of business calls to make."

"I understand, Bassam. Lesley has explained to us that you are so busy with the family business. Welcome to Scotland! We are so looking forward to getting to know you."

"And I you, Alexander."

What an enjoyable evening. Mum had prepared a delightful gourmet meal, accompanied by wonderful wine. The conversation flowed, with lots of laughter and reminiscing. Everyone seemed at ease. I felt surrounded with love by those who were very much part of my life, mum, dad, Aunt Helen, Uncle Gordon and now this wonderful man. Bassam was never short of a story. As I listened to him, I pondered. How could I be so lucky to have met someone who had achieved so much, yet remained so humble? The next few days were just lovely. I was feeling so very happy and content, as I opened up my world, my family and my country to this man bearing so many gifts? A few days later I was leaving to visit London on a three-day trip, to present some management classes to newly promoted employees.

"I will come with you Lesley, and after your classes, we can go for dinner and perhaps go to the movies or take in a show. What do you think?"

"Sounds a great idea, Bassam, it has been such a long time since I attended any venues in London."

Having arrived in London, Bassam arranged our evenings while I conducted my classes. On one of the evenings we went to see a powerful movie called

Sweet November, with Charlize Theron and Keanu Reeves. It was the only time I would ever see Bassam shed a tear. This romantic drama, a great love affair in which the leading actress is diagnosed with terminal cancer. She was dying and Bassam squeezed my hand, his eyes swelling as he shed a tear.

"How sad, Lesley."

"Oh yes Bassam, but look how much she is loved by her man. He has never left her side."

"Like us Lesley, I will always be at your side."

Such a poignant moment for me, not realising that a few years later its poignancy, concerning cancer, would come to light and change my life forever.

On the last night, Bassam took me to a very private, exclusive casino, in Mayfair, which I have since found out he was a member.

"You sit here Lesley," he said, as he pulled a seat out for me at one of the card tables.

"Here is some money for you to play with," he said, as he pulled out a wad of Scottish £100 bank notes from his jacket pocket.

"Sorry Bassam, I have never played before and really I don't know how."

"Okay," he said, "you just watch me."

For the next few hours he played between the card table and the roulette wheel. I honestly felt quite bored and out of my comfort zone, even though I was trying to relax, sipping a coupe of the most expensive champagne. I saw almost five thousand pounds slip through his fingers and still he kept going! At this point I will admit I should have realised there was a lot more to Bassam than meets the eye, but I had fallen in love and I did so want it to work.

This would be another poignant moment in time for me, as a few years later his gambling addiction would come to light, with devastating consequences.

A few days later, I returned to Saudi Arabia to conduct some classes, while Bassam remained in London for business(!), he said.

A few days later he called me, "It was great to have met your mum and dad Lesley, how are things back in Jeddah?"

"Everything is fine here. How is business in London?"

"Business is good."

"By the way Bassam, how are my stocks doing?"

"Everything is going well. In fact, if you wait till December, I will have trebled your money. What do you think?"

"Okay Bassam, I will wait till December and then will you put it back into my Arab Bank saving account?"

"Fabulous Lesley, what an extra special Christmas you will have."

Wedding Bells
November/December 2000

Well, you might be rather surprised but Bassam has just proposed, almost a year to the day from when we first met. He is waiting for me in Egypt and has arranged our wedding there. He wants us to keep it a secret for now, until we have one of the Saudi Royals' permission to actually live as husband and wife in Saudi Arabia, which he says is a formality and will take just a couple of months.

"When we get the Saudi permission papers Lesley, we will have a big party with my family in the Northern Region and live in one of the family mansions there. We will also buy a home in Scotland, in fact I think it would be great to purchase a shooting lodge somewhere up North, in the Perthshire Region. What do you think Lesley, our own little family in Scotland?"

"What about my work, Bassam?"

"You won't have to work anymore. When you become my wife you can help me in my business, perhaps in running the shooting lodge?"

"Oh yes, that sounds wonderful, but I will have to tell mum about our plans, it would break her heart if she didn't know."

"Of course Lesley, and please let her know that we will plan another ceremony, in the Church, for all your family."

"Really Bassam, you would marry me in the Catholic Church?"

"Of course Lesley, I love you."

I am so excited. Everything is coming together. I feel on top of the world.

Bassam explained that we would have a simple ceremony in Egypt, conducted by an Imam, before our church ceremony back in Scotland.

"You will not have to convert to Islam Lesley, because it is stated in the

Koran that a Muslim male is allowed to marry a woman who follows any one of the three holy books, be it Koran, Torah or Bible."

"What about if we have any babies, Bassam?"

"Well, they can have dual passports and learn about both our religions."

Like my Ethiopian friend Anna, there would be no apartheid for Bassam and I.

Tomorrow is the big day. I will catch the early morning flight for the afternoon wedding ceremony in Egypt. I am feeling so excited about this new stage of my life.

Today, I have decided to spend the morning lazing on my balcony, which is adorned with the sweet scents of Jasmine and bougainvillaea, while my Filipino maid, Luz, busily prepares my breakfast.

Of course, over the twenty years my situation has changed, having this prestigious position, I do live a very comfortable and happy life. I live in what one could only describe as a penthouse, situated in a lovely compound near the Red Sea. My apartment is quite beautiful. The décor throughout, in soft pastels, cooling marble floors with scattered, contrasting, brightly-coloured Persian rugs, from distant lands to which I have travelled.

I have two part-time maids; Luz from the Philippines, a wonderful caring woman, and beautiful Shirome from Sri Lanka. They both look after me and whenever I am away on a business trip, they take care of my beautiful little girl, my white Persian cat, Suki. I give them a salary, as the actual company, who brought them to Saudi Arabia through an agent, pay them only a pittance. Sometimes even that is late or so delayed they wonder if they will ever get paid at all. As I have previously mentioned to you the way the majority of the domestic workers are treated here is diabolical and a disgrace. They have virtually no rights. All I can try to do is help them whenever I can.

"Mam Lesley, here is your breakfast."

"Can you believe it Luz? Tomorrow I am getting married."

"Yes Mam, I know."

I turned and looked at Luz.

"What's wrong?" I said, as a noticed a teardrop in her eye.

"I am going to miss you so, Mam Lesley."

"Oh please don't be sad Luz. I am not resigning yet you know. I will be back next week. Listen, I promise, when we have the estate in Perthshire I will send for you to stay with us. You will become our housekeeper. What do you think?" I said, as I got up from my breakfast table.

"Oh yes, Mam, that will be my dream," she said, giving me the biggest hug.

"Well, that's settled then Luz, and if I have a baby, well I just know that you will be the best nanny in the world."

"Oh, thank you Mam," said Luz, with the biggest smile.

"Now, that's better young lady," I said softly. "Why don't you and Shirome join me for coffee tomorrow morning, before I leave?"

"Yes Mam, that would be lovely."

"Good, then I will ask the driver to bring us some of those delicious pastries from the Lebanese Patisserie."

"Thank you Mam, I will leave you now, to enjoy your breakfast, while I go and prepare your suitcase. You will look so beautiful, Mam Lesley, in your cream Chanel suit."

"Thank you Luz see you tomorrow."

Sipping my coffee, I start to take stock of how lucky I have been in my life till now. The views from my balcony window are stunning, with carefully tendered lawns, palm trees standing tall, colourful desert blossoms with pinks and yellows of the bougainvillea, and the pretty whites and creams of jasmine and honeysuckle. In the evenings the flowers produce the most mystical fragrance and scents of Arabia. The swimming pool is shimmering like crystal, under the glare of the sun, as though beckoning me to take a morning dip in her refreshing waters.

"Salaam Alaykum, Mam Lesley," I hear, as I look over the balcony, from the trusted and unassuming figure, working amongst the foliage. Mr Ahmed is a gentle and kind Egyptian man and is the one responsible for all this beauty and colour.

"Alaykum Salaam, Mr Ahmed," I replied, with a smile. "Thank you so much, for the wonderful work you do in the gardens."

His face lit up. "Thank you, Mam Lesley," he said, as he continued to prune some roses in the shrubbery.

Suki, my beautiful Persian cat, is outstretched on the balcony, under the shade of the bougainvillaea, like me, enjoying the early morning sun. She had been a rescue cat. The poor wee thing had been declawed and no longer able to defend herself. Unfortunately, Saudi Arabia is a country which has no animal rights legislation. Protection of animals is definitely not part of the Saudi psyche, in fact, reaching zero on their Richter scale. But now, this wee girl is mine. I will keep her safe; no one would ever hurt her again. Contentedly, I close my eyes, feeling the warmth of the desert sun on my face, realising that from tomorrow my life would change, but what a wonderful life I have had till now!

Having arrived in Egypt and while getting ready for my wedding ceremony I feel quite pretty in my Chanel suit and satin shoes, with diamantes. Bassam is looking quite dapper, dressed in western attire with a yellow silk tie. The driver is taking us downtown in Cairo to the building where the Imam will conduct our wedding ceremony. It is ever so simple, just Bassam, three witnesses and the Imam. I couldn't believe it, thirty minutes later and we are leaving with our marriage license and a gold band on my finger. The driver then whisks us off to the Sheraton Hotel where Bassam has arranged a quiet celebration dinner. The elegant Tuscany restaurant, with about twenty tables, had been closed off just for us. We are greeted and congratulated by the management and staff.

"Congratulations to you, Mr Bassam and Madam, we do hope you enjoy your evening with us."

Bassam made me feel so special, as our favourite music by Andrea Bocelli was played in our honour. We sat at the table with the most elaborate flower display. The waiters looked after our every wish, with champagne, wine, caviar and succulent lobster.

"Well Lesley, how do you feel?"

"Oh, I feel so wonderful. You have planned this day so perfectly for us".

"This is just the beginning Lesley. Wait till you see the beautiful ceremony we will have in Saudi Arabia and of course with your family in Scotland."

After our celebration dinner, Bassam suggested that we go into the hotel casino. As we entered the majestic casino, Bassam was greeted by everyone.

"Hello Mr Bassam, here is a table for you and Madam."

"What would you like to drink?"

"My usual malt whisky please."

"And for madam?"

"A glass of Chardonnay please."

"Gosh, Bassam, everyone knows you here."

"Yes Lesley, we, the family, are well known in Egypt because of our businesses and properties. In fact, tonight we will be staying at one of our properties, the family villa in Maadi."

"Where is Maadi, Bassam?"

"It is a beautiful leafy suburb in Cairo, with its grand villas and mansions; very exclusive and very expensive."

"Who lives there?"

"No one is there at the moment. The family use it as a holiday retreat when we visit. We have one of our drivers and maids living there, who keep it in pristine condition, preparing it for any of the family's arrival. They are expecting us this evening, and the maid will look after your every need. Lesley I am sorry, but there is something I have to mention to you?"

"What's that Bassam?"

"I know you are close with your maids back in Saudi Arabia but in my family we do not get close to them. They are employed to work for us and please, remember never to discuss family issues with them."

"Yes, I realise not to discuss private issues, but as for the rest why, they are people just like you and me?"

He took my hand, "That's just the way it is, you must follow decorum Lesley. The family domestics are not our friends. You have a husband now, so if you are not sure about anything please ask me."

At this point I felt a little mystified by what Bassam was saying. He knew and always said till now what a great relationship I had with my own maids. Perhaps he is just being a gallant caring husband. I convinced myself that was the case. I realise marriage is a compromise, we will both just have to learn to give and take, I suppose?

Bassam spent time at the gaming tables, while I relaxed in one of the comfy armchairs with my glass of wine, observing the, so called, elite of the city.

"I have won a lot of money tonight Lesley. Look, a few thousand dollars."

"Wow, you are so lucky"

"Yes Lesley, I am indeed."

A little later the driver took us home to the villa. It was massive, with marbled floors and high ceilings. The door was opened by the maid, who guided us through to a very grand room with ornate tables, chairs and huge comfy sofas to relax on.

"Would you care for some tea Madam?"

"Yes, thank you, that would be lovely."

The driver brought our luggage and took it directly to our private rooms.

"Lesley, I have to make some calls, please feel at home. The maid will show you our private quarters when you are ready."

"Thank you, Bassam."

The maid brought me some mint tea as I relaxed, trying to take in all the grandeur surrounding me. Half an hour passed

"Madam you must be feeling tired, may I show you through to your quarters?"

"Yes, thank you, that would be lovely."

It was quite a walk to our en suite bedroom, and even though it was very clean and elegant, there was still a musty smell, signifying to me that it had been a long time since this part of the house had been occupied. The maid had already unpacked my suitcase. My clothes were hanging neatly while my lotions and perfumes had been placed carefully on the most elaborate, cream-coloured dressing table, with gold trim.

"Madam, may I help you get dressed for bed?"

"No, thank you," I said.

"May I help you remove your jewellery?"

"No, I can manage, thank you. That will be all."

"Of course Madam, Good night."

"Good night," I replied.

Bassam soon finished his calls and retired to our private quarters.

"Well Lesley, how are you feeling?"

"I feel so loved and rather pampered Bassam."

"Well you better get used to it, this is only the beginning!"

The next morning, over a delicious traditional Egyptian breakfast of egg shahouka, accompanied by delicious warm baladi bread and sweet tea, we planned our day. We would visit Bassam's private clay pigeon shooting club, have lunch and meet some of his friends. Just before leaving the villa, I opened my purse and to my surprise and disbelief I realised about 1,000 Saudi Riyals (£200) was missing from my purse.

"Bassam, I have some money missing from my purse."

"Are you sure, Lesley?"

"Yes I am sure. I had 2,000 Saudi Riyals and now there is only 1,000 left."

"When did you last look at your purse?"

"Last night, here in the villa."

"Okay, let me talk to the maid and driver."

"Surely Bassam they wouldn't do this, you told me that they were very trustworthy and had been with your family for years?"

"Well that's true Lesley, but who else could it have been?"

Ten minutes later Bassam returned to our private quarters saying he had talked to both the maid and driver.

"Lesley, unfortunately the driver has said that it was he who took your money from your purse and he is very sorry."

"Did you ask for it back Bassam?"

I will deal with it later, don't worry. We left the villa to enjoy our day in the beautiful Egyptian city. I tried to forget the incident, although I could never feel comfortable again in the presence of the driver. How strange, I thought, my first night in the villa, my honey moon and I get robbed. Bassam said he dealt with the matter, but my stolen money was never returned and the driver remains at work? Oh Well, who knows why he did it, rather strange but I don't want to wallow, I just want to enjoy this time with my new husband!

A few weeks later Bassam and I travel to Scotland to be with my family for Christmas. He is so welcomed by all my family, who make such a fuss of him and what a lovely time it was. After the festivities, the two of us decide to travel up north to Perthshire to have another look at any country homes for sale, and at the same time Bassam can attend some shoots. A magical three weeks has come to an end as I need to get back to work in Saudi Arabia.

"I will stay on in Scotland, Lesley, with your parents, and take them to look at some country homes that are up for sale. At the same time, when you go back to Saudi Arabia you can resign if you want to and we will start our marriage, living together here in Scotland, till our Saudi marriage permission papers arrive. I so want to take you home to meet the rest of my family, so hopefully it will not take long."

"That would be great, mum and dad will so enjoy travelling with you to see these country homes. It will be a wee adventure for them."

"Well yes Lesley, they are my mum and dad now too and I was thinking that when we find our new home, if your parents wish, they can come and live with us. I will make sure they have a part of the house as their own

"That would be fantastic. I so want to continue looking after my parents."

"I know you do Lesley, and after you resign I will take on that mantle."

I am now back in Saudi Arabia and have handed in my resignation, as you can imagine it is such a big step after all these years of being so independent. Financially, I have a nice indemnity when I leave. Bassam has said I will not have to worry about money again and just look forward to having our own family in Scotland. I feel so loved, content and secure.

We are talking daily on the phone.

"Lesley, I have seen some beautiful houses up north, and one in Arran that

I think you might like. When are you able to return to Scotland and view them?"

"I finish at the end of April."

"Okay Lesley, I will wait for you. There are so many houses coming up in the market. Here's your mum."

"Have you liked some of the houses that you have seen with Bassam, Mum."

"Oh yes Lesley, although they really are very big. The one the other day was by a river full of salmon."

"Oh fabulous mum, well I will be seeing you soon, all of you take care."

"Hold on Lesley, here is Bassam".

"Lesley, I have been attending the mosque and have met some nice people and guess what, I am selling some land in Saudi Arabia to buy our house here in Scotland. My brother, Talal, is looking after it for me. My mother and sisters are so looking forward to you coming home to meet them. Hopefully the permission papers for you to live there will be ready soon and I have rented out my home in America, so we will have another income coming in."

"Oh fabulous Bassam, well done you."

"How is your packing going for leaving, have you arranged your tickets?"

"Yes, I will travel back through London and my maids are packing as we speak."

"Okay Lesley, I will go now. I have a meeting this afternoon. I will tell you all about it when I see you. Take care."

A few days have passed and I am a little bit on edge. Having resigned, in three days' time I am supposed to travel back to Scotland to start my new life with Bassam; however, he has just called me to say that tomorrow he will be in Dubai and I need to change my airline tickets; instead of travelling to London I should now join him in Dubai.

"Lesley, I have explained to your parents that my brother, Talal, wants us to go to Dubai for a few months, as they need me to handle some business. Tomorrow, I am travelling there to find us a nice place to live."

"Gosh Bassam, it is such short notice. It will be so difficult to rearrange my tickets and Suki will need the appropriate quarantine papers for Dubai."

"Don't worry Lesley, I will call your VIP manager in Saudi Arabia to rearrange your tickets. It will not be a problem, he is a friend of the family and I will make sure that Suki is able to enter with the correct quarantine papers. Remember, it is only for a few months and we can still fly back to Britain regularly to see your parents. In the meantime, you can spend the time relaxing on the beach enjoying all that Dubai sunshine."

"Well yes, Bassam, it does sound rather nice, since I am not working any more, it will be so wonderful to just relax."

"Good Lesley, then your tickets will be changed tomorrow."

"I miss you Bassam ..." the phone went silent. Oh dear, he must have got cut off!

The next day the VIP manager congratulated me on my marriage and wished me good luck in my new life. My travel papers are now ready to travel to Dubai and little Suki has authorisation to enter. That same night Bassam calls saying that he has found us a beautiful apartment and that he will meet us tomorrow at the airport.

It's my last day in Jeddah. The training centre has given me a farewell party.

"We are all going to miss you sweet lady," said my manager, Mr Awadi.

"You will be forever in our hearts," said Assistant Manager and my friend, Halima.

"I will miss you all. It has been such a wonderful life, thank you everyone."

That evening Bassam called me while I was doing my last bit of shopping in the souq.

"Are you ready for your trip, Lesley?"

"Yes I am in the souq to treat myself?"

"What do you mean?"

"Well as you know I have my final indemnity, so I want to treat myself and buy a pair of diamond earrings."

"Oh Lesley, why don't you just keep your money? I have already bought you the most beautiful pair of two carat, diamond studs."

"Oh really!"

"Yes Lesley, just keep your money. You really don't have to spend it now. I have to go. I will see you tomorrow at the airport."

It's a beautiful morning as the aircraft takes off. Higher and higher we go, under a magnificent blue sky with the occasional fluffy white cloud. My beautiful wee girl Suki is in her carrier on the seat beside me. Can you imagine how I feel, relaxing on this aircraft, no longer an employee, but now a married lady? My husband waiting for me in Dubai, someone who says he will cherish me forever and, after working so hard all these years, I think I am going to enjoy being pampered.

I have become quite accustomed to the thought, that I will never have to work again, just look after my husband, Suki and hopefully one day I will have my own wee bairns and help Bassam run the shooting lodge back in bonnie Scotland. Yes, I think, I have done okay.

Landing at Dubai International airport, the crew say a final goodbye.

"We will all miss you, Miss Lesley, please remember us."

"Always," I smiled, "Goodbye."

Suki and I passed through the airport and there, waiting after the customs area, was Bassam.

"Welcome to Dubai, Lesley, how was your trip?"

"It was great, but I will be glad to get Suki out of her carrier."

"Lesley this is the driver. Unfortunately, our apartment is still being decorated and so we will be staying at the Hilton Hotel for a few days."

"But what about Suki?"

"My goodness, she is only a cat Lesley, we will just have to smuggle her somehow into the hotel."

Well folks, that is what I did. For what turned out to be a week in the Hilton I managed to hide my wee girl in the room. What a start but I am sure it can only get better?

Today, at last, we are checking out of the hotel. Bassam left early for a business meeting and just before the hotel checkout time he called me.

"Sorry Lesley, I am delayed at the meeting, please checkout of the room and pay the bill with your credit card."

"But Bassam, where will I wait, I have Suki with me?"

"Just put her in her container and wait in the foyer. I won't be long."

Three hours passed and eventually Bassam arrived in the foyer.

"Sorry Lesley, I had a crucial meeting to attend on behalf of Talal."

I could see that he was nervous, so I just left it at that. Although between you and me, I am feeling a little bit anxious about his spontaneity and so many business meetings. Oh well, I suppose I just have to remind myself that marriage is a compromise and we still have a lot to learn about each other.

To my disappointment the apartment is in downtown Dubai and not a very nice area, certainly not as Bassam had described. It certainly was not beside the beautiful Al Jumerah Beach and there was no swimming pool. It was a one bedroomed flat. The inside looking quite worn and rather dated to say the least. The balcony overlooked a busy road and then into other flats in the same state.

"Lesley, I am sorry this is not quite what you expected, but I was so short of time. I promise we will move as soon as I find something in Al Jumeira beach district."

"Really Bassam, I am not a snob, but this is not a good area."

Sure enough, from the balcony during the day my views were washing lines and in the evening on the street below `the women of the night on duty`. It certainly wasn't my balcony adorned with blossoms, with the gardener Mr Ahmed smiling amongst the foliage wishing me a "Good Morning."

A few days later Bassam is taking me to meet a couple; the husband being a contact he made at a business function.

"They are from Norway, Lesley. He is such a lovely man. They have invited us to dinner tomorrow night at their home and guess where they live?"

"Where?" I asked.

"At Al Jumeira beach. So, I was thinking, you can see the villa they live in and if you like it then I will get us something there."

At last, I thought, thank goodness. I really have to get out of this place it's such a dive and I don't want to live here anymore.

"Great Bassam," I said, realising that anything would be better than this.

What a beautiful and sincere couple they were, Frederik and Ane. They were a little older, perhaps late sixties. Frederik himself still working as a Scientist for a Norwegian company based in Dubai. Their home was a beautiful villa. Not too elaborate nor too big. The ambience of soothing colours and scattered rugs over marble floors was so relaxing and felt like home. (Does it sound familiar?) It was obvious Ane and I had similar tastes and passions. Her floral displays in crystal vases, scattering of home and garden magazines, family photos, and comfy sofas with plumped up colourful cushions made it so cosy and welcoming.

"Let me show you the garden and pool, Lesley."

"How beautiful Ane," I said, as she opened the French windows into a beautiful and well-tended garden. Colourful blossoms were everywhere surrounding a small pool; its surface adorned with some loose flowers that had fallen from the nearby bougainvillea.

"Oh Ane your home is so beautiful; it so reminds me of my home before my marriage."

"How long have you been married, Lesley?"

"Oh, just a few months. Bassam is searching for a villa in this area, I do hope he finds something soon."

"Well Lesley, that would be lovely. We could be neighbours and please remember, till then you can visit anytime."

"Thank you, Ane I would like that."

Two weeks later, I was travelling back to Scotland to meet my family. Ane kindly looked after Suki. Bassam didn't come with me as he said he had a lot of work and still was looking for our villa.

On return to Dubai, I was sad to find out Bassam hadn't yet found us a new place and some woman from Australia had been staying at our flat while I was away. How do I know this you might ask? Well I found a letter from her to Bassam thanking him for the lovely week.

"Who is she Bassam?"

"A friend of the family, Lesley, she knows Talal?"

For the first time I felt hurt. Was it true what he told me? I am not a stupid woman. I love Bassam, I have given up my career for him and I so wanted and needed to believe him.

The following morning, I went to Ane's and collected Suki.

"Thank you so very much Ane for looking after my wee girl," I said as I gave her a beautiful Scottish thistle, crystal vase, as a thank you.

"Oh thank you Lesley, how beautiful, I will always keep your vase filled with flowers from my garden and always think of you my lovely new friend. You really didn't have to bring me anything; she was a pleasure to look after. Any time you are travelling, don't hesitate to bring her to me."

"Oh thank you so very much Ane. That is good to know."

One week passed and Ane and I arranged to catch up and have coffee at one of the shopping malls.

"Your husband is wanting to do some business with Frederick, Lesley, in fact they are meeting today."

"Really Ane, I didn't realise, he must have forgotten to tell me. What type of business?"

"Bassam has mentioned building a business portfolio for leasing villas here to foreigners. He has told Frederick about all the experience he has through his own lands and projects he shares with his brothers back in Saudi Arabia."

"Oh well," I said rather surprised, "hopefully it will be a fruitful meeting for both of them."

We arranged to meet for lunch the following week, but I never heard from Ane again. I left voicemails but she never got back to me.

"They have probably left the country Lesley," said Bassam.

"But she would have told me, we had become such good friends."

Why I asked myself, how can they have just left? I know Ane would have said goodbye. Were they upset about something? Did something happen between Bassam and Frederick? As usual Bassam is tight lipped and saying nothing.

Months pass and Bassam is still waiting for the sale of some of his land. In the meantime, there is no change to our circumstances. I do the housework, cooking and laundry, although I have found a maid who pops in once a week to help me if needed. I pay her once a month. In fact, have been paying most of the bills. My indemnity is gradually depleting. I spend a lot of time on my own as Bassam keeps travelling for business, back to Saudi Arabia. Recently, I was so very upset with him because, on his trip to Abu Dhabi, he left without paying any bills even though I had given him the money. Living in a crappy apartment is bad enough and now our electricity has been turned off.

I called him, "Bassam, are you still in Abu Dhabi? The electricity has been turned off because you haven't paid the bill."

"Sorry Lesley, I am in the middle of a meeting and will be back the day after tomorrow."

"That's not good enough Bassam. It is very hot, we can hardly breathe, Bassam are you there? The phone went dead."

Suki and I were left in the dark and without ventilation for the next two days. As his wife I was unable to deal with the household bills as they were all in his name. What have I done? Perhaps Bassam is not the man I thought he was. I am starting to feel quite anxious.

Time passes, the Saudi permission marriage papers for me have not yet been finalised, I am still living in the crappy apartment, my indemnity money has almost depleted, I have received no money from the stocks and shares, and I never did receive my wedding gift of diamond earrings, surprise!

Everything seems to be at a standstill!

Two nights later Bassam came through the door.

"Hi Honey, how are you?"

"How am I Bassam? Now you ask. Why did you cut the telephone while I was talking to you the other day?"

"I am sorry Lesley; I had forgotten to power my mobile."

"Bassam it's almost a year now and nothing is happening. I am running out of money. Where is all this money going?"

"Lesley, I have just spoken to Talal and he expects a sale of my land any day."

"I am sorry Bassam but everything just seems to be moving so slowly and this flat is just not acceptable anymore. You are travelling so much on business trips, but you never seem to make any money from these deals. What is going on?"

"Oh Lesley, that's not fair. So, what you are saying is that it is alright for you to live like a princess in a country home when all my money comes from my land sales, but your money is just for you?"

"No Bassam, you know that is not what I mean. If I hadn't married you I would have continued in my successful career. At this moment in time, I am sorry, but everything you said before we married has not materialised and if something doesn't happen soon, I will have run out of money and not be able to sustain us anymore. I am scared!"

"Yes Lesley, I understand what you are saying, but soon my money will come from the land, in fact Talal has said the money should be in my account in a couple of weeks. I was thinking it's time to start packing up and we will travel back home to Scotland and stay with your parents for the next week or two until the money comes through? Please Lesley, be patient for just a few more weeks!"

Well, we are now back in Scotland, staying with my parents until the land sale money arrives. It is so lovely back home and being near my dear mum. I have left Suki with my maid, for a couple of weeks, until we finalise the land sale.

We have decided to hold our wedding celebration next month. I have chosen my dress, ivory satin with an encrusted jewelled top and tiara. The celebration invitations have gone out. Bassam is delivering them personally to his family as he has been requested by Talal to go over to Saudi Arabia to meet up with family lawyers regarding his affairs as he will now be spending less time there and more in Scotland. At the same time, he will be able to finalise our Saudi Arabian marriage papers.

It's one month to go and everything is in order. The wedding venue is near Loch Lomond, a magnificent country home situated on acres of land. Every window captures beautiful views of the loch and hopefully it will be a sunny September day. We are anticipating around 100 guests on my side and I am waiting for Bassam to confirm numbers on his side.

Our day has arrived. Bassam is looking so handsome in his kilt, as does his best man who has just flown in from Lebanon. We could hear the stirring Scottish melodies in the distance as the piper greets the guests who have started to arrive. I feel wonderful as we are piped into the celebration room to meet everyone. A few photo shots on the magnificent lawns, followed by a scrumptious three course meal. What a celebration, and to close the evening a quartet played through the night as our guests danced into the wee hours. That night when all the guests were gone Bassam and I retired to our honeymoon suite.

"Well Lesley, did you enjoy the celebration?"

"Oh yes Bassam, it was wonderful. Only I am sad that none of your family could make it."

"Lesley, please don't be sad. They wanted to be here but mum is just too ill."

"Yes I understand that, I just wish one of them had made it."

"Emile and James were here and so many other of our other friends jetted in."

"Yes, I know Bassam, but they are not family."

Nothing more was said.

Some time passes and at last Bassam's money for the business is starting to be transferred from Saudi Arabia. He has a monthly allowance from the family business, how much I don't know as questions about his money are a sensitive subject. I realise that perhaps I should take the 'bull by the horns' but he keeps saying that it is just a waiting game until all the money arrives. I know that in Saudi Arabia the wheels often turn in very slow motion, but my goodness this is becoming ridiculous. I am beginning to feel like Methuselah. I am trying so hard not to be confrontational, but I now have no money left of my own and having to depend on someone totally for all my needs and continue to trust them after such a long time of broken promises is very stressful.

We have moved into a trendy apartment in Glasgow and tomorrow I am travelling back to Dubai to get my wee girl Suki. Oh gosh how I so miss my wee girl! Four days later I return to Scotland with Suki, now in quarantine, and I am exhausted.

At dinner that night, Bassam asked, "How much will the quarantine cost?"

"£1,000 but I will be putting it on my gold card."

Suddenly he said, "Lesley, please sit down, I am so very sorry."

Bassam took my hand.

"You know I love you, don't you?"

"Yes, although recently Bassam I have been a bit worried. I thought you didn't care for me so much anymore. You spend so much time travelling and leaving me on my own."

"Lesley, it is going to be different very soon. Like it was when I first met you but I have made a big mistake."

"What Bassam, you're scaring me. What's wrong?"

"Remember when you ordered me a supplementary gold card. Well, I am sorry, there is nothing left on it."

"Don't be silly Bassam, there was £8,000 on it four days ago and I haven't used it"

"Yes Lesley, I understand that but I got carried away and spent it."

"On what?" I asked.

With sorrow in his face he held up a pamphlet which said 'Gambler's Anonymous'.

"What does this mean, Bassam?"

"I have lost all your money. I am so sorry, please forgive me. I am now attending Gam Anon."

"What is Gam Anon?" I asked.

"It's somewhere you can go to talk to someone when you feel you have been gambling too much and want to stop."

"What do you mean gambling too much. When have you had time to gamble?"

"When on my business trips," he said.

"Do you mean you're an addict, Bassam?"

"Of course not, please don't insult me?"

"I am certainly not trying to insult you Bassam, but £8,000 in three days? My God you know how hard I have worked in the Saudi desert to build my life before I met you. If you carry on like this, it will destroy me."

"It was just this one time; I realise I have made a big mistake. I will put the money back on your card in the next few days."

"But what if it happens again?"

"I promise it won't Lesley. There is too much at stake. I have talked to Gam Anon. It was just a terrible error and it will not happen again. Please don't tell anyone Lesley, I am so embarrassed!"

Note to Reader:,

Please, don't think I am too naive a person, but at this point I knew nothing about gambling although I was so annoyed with the fact that he had gambled £8,000 in four days, while I was in Dubai. I concluded that as he had met up with someone from Gambler's Anonymous for advice he really would be okay and that would be the end of it.

But dah! Silly me, this £8,000 was only the tip of the ice-berg. I certainly didn't realise that because of who Bassam really was and how he would eventually treat me, my life would soon be in a downward spiral and I would end up on my knees!

A few months have passed and Bassam has been showing me a bit more tenderness. We have been socialising a lot with my family and some of his friends. The man that I had originally fallen in love with seems to be back. The land deal closure, he says, will be any day and as most of my funds have dried up, we are living on his monthly allowance from the family business in Saudi Arabia; the exact amount of which he has still has not confided in me. In the meantime, I have now got a job with a fledgling Scottish airline as training and recruitment manager. It is owned by a private businessman and my salary is good. So, this will give me a little bit more independence and I am doing something which I enjoy.

"Lesley you have been so patient waiting for my money from the land deal, I promise soon you will be a lady of leisure."

"Oh yes Bassam, I hope so, it really is time to start the little family we talked about."

"Yes Lesley, talking about family, I think it's time that we approached Father McBride to make preparations for our marriage in the church. I know this will make your mum so happy. What do you think?"

Sure enough to my delight we had a church wedding in Saint Thomas's church, our marriage blessed by father McBride in front of friends and close family members, on a beautiful summers day. I felt so at peace as we both made our vows.

'To love and protect each other,
For richer, for poorer,
In sickness and in health,
Till death us do part'

The teething troubles in our marriage seem to be over. Bassam is being so kind and gentle. We have made our vows to each other in the church and the money for the shooting estate is on its way. Some time has passed and we are now living in the centre of Glasgow in a very elegant listed building. The foyer is of beautiful marble with a private lift to twelve luxury penthouses. Our neighbour, a Baroness, is rather a nice lady. We take tea together and I enjoy listening to her speak about her travels, like I used to do, to faraway lands. Bassam has bought two of the penthouses.

"As soon as I buy this third penthouse Lesley, we will rent all three out and then move to the countryside for our shooting estate."

"Bassam, you are doing so well. I am so proud of you."

"Thank you Lesley, now you know why I have to travel to Saudi Arabia and have to spend so much time away on business appointments. Please remember, if anything happens to me you will be a comfortable woman."

I am still working and my contribution to the household is my giving

Bassam £600 per month for health insurance, so if either of us ever get sick we are insured for half a million pounds.

"Lesley, why don't you stop working now and start to travel with me on some of my business trips. We will be okay. You don't have to work anymore?"

"Really Bassam, but if I stop working I have no more money. It's all gone while waiting for your land. I am not complaining, but do you think we are okay?"

"For goodness sake Lesley, look what I have done for you, of course we are okay. I feel hurt Lesley. It sounds that you don't want to spend more time with me?"

"Oh Bassam, don't be silly, of course I do."

"Then let's start to enjoy our life together, like it was when we first dated."

"I will just have to give them one month's notice, beginning next Monday."

"Okay Lesley, fantastic, then let's go out and celebrate."

Note to Reader:

I left my job, but as time goes on, as before, I am again starting to feel isolated and alone. It is as though my husband is a Doctor Jekyll and Mr Hyde. You might have guessed by now who and what he is. Again, I am repeating, I am not a shrinking violet, but when you love someone so much, sometimes you only see what you want to see and not what is actually happening. Like being in a goldfish bowl; one's vision becomes blurred.

October 2008

I am so very exhausted, the lies, the women, the gambling, and the verbal abuse is now becoming physical. Bassam projects himself to people outside as an accomplished business man, who is pious and a great husband. As for business, we will lose everything if the gambling doesn't stop. As for pious, he never goes to the Mosque, except to make business contacts. The women with whom he frequents, some of whom are obviously prostitutes. I have seen the texts between him and them. Can you believe, it he calls himself Dodi or Stephen when meeting these women? I am left in the lower penthouse, alone, while looking after the running of the upper penthouse which we have rented out, while he is spending all the money we are making on his vices. I cannot tell my parents about this, it would so hurt my mum and I feel so embarrassed by his antics and what he really is. He gives me a pittance of money to buy food and I have to use my own credit cards just to put food on the table. I am unable to buy new clothes and haven't had a holiday abroad in years. I need to deal with him somehow and get back my money which I gave him and he has squandered. This includes the six thousand pounds I gave him recently, which was a gift to me from my parents. I gave him this money as a loan for setting up a new business but I should have learned as, just like before, he has gambled it all away. I must think straight, no more seeing through rose tinted spectacles. I just hope it is not too late! First thing I should do is set up my own business. I really need to think this out.

My father has loaned me some money in order that I can set up a business and escape this spider's web. So folks, I am now off to China with my friend Min Chen, who is studying to become a corporate banker. We have got contracts with some Scottish universities and colleges to find them new students in China. What a wonderful three-week trip Min and I had, from the minute we landed at Beijing Airport, immediately followed by another three-hour flight to Min's home town of Fuzhou. Her family are so hospitable, as were the people of her town and, even though to say the least we are rather jet lagged, we have started interviewing the candidates. On the final few days of our trip we travelled by boat for a relaxing break to the most beautiful sunshine island of Wu Lang Yu, the 'Island of pearls'. My goodness, their treasures are so beautiful, such big pearls and so many colours. The alleyways of shops display beautiful jewellery of diamonds and emeralds combined with these magnificent pearls, according to the buyer's request. What another great business idea, we smiled to ourselves. Perhaps in the future?

On return to Scotland we are both pleased with what we have done and the following month we will be meeting with the relevant institutions to finalise contracts. I am feeling so happy, realising that now, once again, I have been given the chance to become 'a woman of substance' and escape from the torment of abuse which I am suffering. A few days of rest after my trip and I am still feeling a little tired. Bassam, as usual, is away for a few days. There is no point in quizzing him about where he is, as all I will get told are lies. I just need to keep my head low to stealthily and quietly build myself a new life.

The next morning, I wake up and poor Suki has hurt her leg. It is bleeding. She must have jumped off the table or on to one of the surfaces last night. I bathed her leg, she seems fine and snuggles down. However, that afternoon she gets worse and I rush her in a taxi to the vets.

Arriving at the vet and after some examinations, I hear from the vet what I have dreaded.

"I am sorry, Mrs Sehli, but Suki has cancer."

"Oh no, can you do anything for her?"

"Well as she is an old cat (around 23 years old), it might be unfair to do much. We would have to remove her leg, which besides everything else would be quite a trauma for her, with no guarantee."

"If I take her home, how long has she got?"

"About a month."

"Thank you, then I will take her home."

The next few days I nursed my wee girl day and night but on the third morning, she started to bleed again and gosh, so much blood. I called Bassam.

"Please wake up Bassam, Suki is really bad."

"Oh shut up about that cat. I had a late night and I'm tired."

"It's already 11.00 o'clock Bassam, please I need you to help me get her in her carrier and go quickly to the vet."

He shouted, "I told you, shut up. Leave me alone, we can go tonight and how much will that cost?"

"Enough about money Bassam," I screamed, "please get up now."

Arriving back at the vets, unfortunately, I had to let my little girl go. She is buried in my parents' garden under the lush yellow laburnum tree, but as I had promised the first day I saw her, no one would ever hurt her again!

The following week I travelled to London spending the weekend to catch up with my very best friend Jenny. Actually, she is like a big sister to me, so kind and thoughtful, and we are always there for each other.

"So Lesley, how are things?"

"I am so very tired Jenny. I have felt like this for a few weeks. I just feel exhausted all the time."

"It's Bassam, he has made your life hell and, of course, you have just lost Suki."

"I know, Jenny, things are so bad."

"Is he still threatening you and pushing you around?"

"Yes Jenny, but please remember, this is our secret."

"Lesley, you need to get help. He has all those guns in the house safe and look at his temper. Has he hit you again?"

"No, not since I lost Suki."

"You really have to report him to the police if he hurts you again. Why don't you just leave him Lesley?"

"With what Jenny? He has taken all my money. I have no job. No, I need more time. Min and I will build the business and when I am more independent, then I will be able to deal with him."

"Lesley you can always come and stay with me."

"Oh I know, my lovely Jenny, but I am not going to run away. I will not be his victim. I have rights."

"Look, I am sure your fatigue is nothing other than stress, but before you deal with him, go to the doctor and get a check-up."

"Yes, I will Jenny."

"Do you promise?"

"Yes, I will make an appointment as soon as I get home."

Black Shadow

I have my appointment today at 11.00 a.m. with my GP, Doctor Muir. I am feeling more tired and keep falling asleep. Last night my left breast was so painful and I felt a lump. I do hope it is nothing serious, we hear so many stories about finding lumps, hopefully it is not the Big C. I am thinking it's probably just stress because of Bassam and his antics. He has been out again all night; goodness knows when he will be back. He's gambling away all the money and continuing with his liaisons. He is depleting our profits from our second penthouse which we are renting out at £2,600 a month. If he was behaving like this in Saudi Arabia and it was discovered, under their laws, he would be severely dealt with. No wonder I am feeling so poorly, this stress is going to kill me, but I must stay strong. Min and I are both quite astute and I know our venture with China will be a success. I must get my life back and then I will be on a strong footing, once again, to deal with Bassam.

The taxi has arrived to take me to Woodside Health Centre, about a 15-minute ride by taxi.

"Good Morning Mrs Sehli," say the two friendly receptionists, Linda and Joanne.

"Good Morning ladies, how are you?"

"We are both great thank you, Mrs Sehli, please take a seat. Doctor Muir will be with you shortly."

The doctor arrives, "Hello Mrs Sehli, this way please."

I follow Doctor Muir through to his bright, welcoming surgery, as he asks me to kindly sit down by his desk.

"Cathy, my nurse, has mentioned that she talked to you on the phone Mrs Sehli and she said that you have not been feeling very well?"

"Yes Doctor Muir I have been feeling so very tired and last night I felt a lump in my breast."

"Please don't worry. If you would kindly go over behind the screen and remove your top. When you are ready just let me know."

As I got ready, I heard Doctor Muir call his lovely nurse, Cathy, into the room. The curtain opened,

"Hello Lesley it's me, Cathy. Are you ready for the Doctor to examine you?"

"Yes, thank you."

During the examination it felt so painful beside the lump.

"Mrs Sehli, how long have you been feeling tired?"

"Oh, I would say a couple of weeks doctor."

"Could it be a cyst?" I asked him.

"Perhaps Mrs Sehli or maybe too much coffee," he smiled.

"Now, please try not to worry. I will send a report to the hospital and make an arrangement for you to go there for a check-up and mammogram. We will send you an appointment date within the next two weeks."

"Thank you, Doctor Muir."

Cathy stayed with me as I dressed.

"Please try not to worry, Lesley, as Doctor Muir has said and remember you can call me anytime."

As I left the surgery my mind began to work overtime, but I couldn't dwell on it, I had other problems to solve. Well, first things first, it's so embarrassing but I don't have enough money to get home. Well, forget a taxi, I don't even have enough money to get a bus. Looks like I will have to walk.

Does fur coat and no knickers ring a bell? Because this is exactly how I am beginning to feel!

I have tried to call Bassam, but as has become more frequent these days he hardly ever answers any of his three mobiles. One does not have to be Einstein to work out why he has a third mobile, the number of which I do not have. However, in the near future my instincts would be proved right, as I accidently came across this third mobile and ended up having a conversation with one of his many concubines. One hour later I reach home exhausted and Bassam is nowhere to be seen. I decided to call my best friend, Jenny.

"Hi Jenny it's me. I just got back from the doctors."

"What did he say Lesley?"

"He confirmed that there is a lump in my breast, but hopefully it will just be a cyst. I will get an appointment within two weeks for a check up."

"You will be okay, Lesley," she said reassuringly.

"Is Bassam there?"

"No."

"Oh dear, Lesley. Have something to eat and then go for a wee sleep. I will call you tonight. I know it is difficult but please try not to worry."

Bassam came back later that night.

"I have been trying to call you, Bassam, since early morning."

"I have been very busy these few days. I told you I had business up north in Perth."

I pretended I believed him, I needed to have him think that I trusted him again, at least until I get my business going and could stand once again on my own two feet.

"I was invited by with one of my friends, who belongs to the Royal family of Dubai. He has bought a house, one of many, which has been built on the grounds of the Gleneagles Hotel. He has agreed to put a bid in on my behalf for one of those houses. Wouldn't it be great to live there Lesley? We would be able to use all the facilities the hotel had to offer."

"My, it sounds so wonderful," I told him, although by this time I already knew he was nothing but a gambler and a liar and this would be just one of his many stories.

"Yes, we will have our own small estate with shooting, falconry and fishing, right on our door step."

"Sounds great, Bassam," I said, while looking at the near empty fridge and thinking of the long walk back from the doctor's surgery I had taken earlier that day.

"So why were you calling me? What was so urgent?"

"I had to go the doctor this morning as I haven't been feeling very well for the last couple of weeks. I have a lump on my breast and I am very worried."

"Oh, it will be nothing," he said, as he left to go through to the kitchen.

"I feel so stressed, Bassam. Why don't you ever answer your mobile. What if I had an emergency or got really sick, and needed to contact you?"

Without turning back, he abruptly stormed along the hallway to the master bedroom shouting,

"Then dial 999."

"Why are you so disrespectful to me Bassam? I am not feeling well."

He turned with such a look of loathing and said, "Grow up," as he slammed the door closed behind him. What a mistake, I thought, meeting and marrying this man. Such a liar; not just a Walter Mitty but an evil manipulator. At this moment in time, I have made my bed and will have to lie in it, but hopefully soon I will be able to get out of this mess.

Waiting for my letter to arrive felt like eternity. I was becoming more tired and my breast was so swollen that I began to feel like Quasimodo. One week passed and then, to my relief, my letter has arrived for an appointment at the Glasgow Western Infirmary, next Thursday at 9.00 a.m., for a mammogram. I called Jenny to tell her the news.

"Good Lesley, would you like me to fly up from London and be with you?"

"Oh thank you Jenny but there is really no need. I'm sure a quick mammogram and then, hopefully, it will be all over. I can then get on with building my new business with Min"

"Okay, but if you change your mind I can be with you at any time."

"Thank you, I know that, but please remember it is still our secret. I don't want anyone to know."

"What about your mum, Lesley?"

"No, I don't want to worry her. I will wait and, hopefully, after the mammogram, there will be nothing to tell her anyway."

"I understand Lesley; it will remain our secret."

It's a lovely sunny winter's day as I take the subway this morning from Buchannan Street in the City Centre of Glasgow to my hospital appointment in the West End. I so enjoy the West End with its appealing little shops aligning Byres Road, reminiscent of a bygone age. Visit one of the bistros or sit outside one of the cafes, relaxing with a cappuccino, you can watch the world go by. Its vibrant colours and sounds echo through the alleyways. Or, take a trip to Ashton Lane with its cobbled street and sip a glass of wine while listening to the latest jazz sounds, catching up with friends and blethering into the wee hours. I always feel upbeat and happy after spending time there. Today, of course, is a little bit different. I have my hospital appointment at 09.00 a.m., so I have plenty time as it's just a ten-minute walk from the subway to the hospital. On reaching the hospital, I go straight to the reception desk and give them my appointment letter.

Not far from the reception is a small tea and coffee shop run by volunteers. There are three friendly ladies working there and what a lovely selection of sandwiches, homemade cakes and biscuits they have on display.

"Good morning, dear," says one, "would you like a wee tea or coffee?"

"Oh yes, thank you, may I have a black coffee?"

"Certainly, lovely day outside," she said, as she gave me my coffee in a gorgeous china coffee cup with matching saucer.

"Oh my, how posh," I said.

"We like to give our best, dear" she smiled.

"Thank you," I said as I gave her the money. "Please keep the change" I told her, knowing full well it couldn't be going to a better cause than these wonderful volunteers, who I would soon realise are very much part of our National Health Service. I am feeling quite relaxed, sipping my coffee, as I wait for my name to be called. Although it's still early the waiting area is becoming quite busy. Nurses are periodically calling out the names of people, who are then led to different rooms along a small corridor. Most of the people waiting have someone with them, but as you know, I didn't want to worry anybody, and although Bassam knows I had an appointment this morning, well, as you might have surmised by now, he just doesn't care. As usual, he is still in bed after being out all night. (Poor him, the casino must have exhausted him after yet again taking all his money, or, shall I rephrase, our money?)

Today, I am meeting mum for lunch at 1.00 p.m. in our favourite book shop in the town centre, Robert Owen's, which has a cosy wee coffee shop. It is a Thursday ritual for mum and I, after her weekly hairdressing appointment. Her hairdresser is John Shaunessey of Glasgow, a handsome man with his salt and pepper hair and trendy gear. Fifty years in the in the trade; he must have started when he was a bairn. He really does create the latest fashion trends, keeping all the ladies in tip top condition. His assistant is his Aunt Alice, amazingly, in her seventies and a wonderfully sprightly character. She is an Eastender lass, like mum and I. Always dressed immaculately and never a hair out of place. She gives you a warm welcome, a kind smile and offer of tea or coffee with of course the customary chocolate biscuit. She is the one responsible for your shampoo and how I love her wee head massage. Mum adores her pampering session and catching up with the latest gossip with all the other ladies. It's the real Glasgow banter, which is priceless. How I enjoy hearing about all the ladies and their latest exploits. Mum and I so enjoy this private time together.

So, I can relax. I have plenty of time. I am sure I won't be more than one hour between seeing the doctor and the mammogram? One of the nurses, standing at the front of reception with a file in her hand, is looking rather perplexed. She keeps looking around and then glancing back to the file. She smiles as one of her colleagues joins her. I think she needs some help in finding the file's owner. I bet you they are looking for me; this happens regularly because of my name. After two tries one of the nurses gets it right and calls out, "Mrs Sehli."

"Good Morning," she says, as I approach her.

"I am so sorry that I wasn't quite able to pronounce your name."

"Oh," I smiled "that's okay, it happens all the time."

"Would you like to come this way?" she said, as she led me down the corridor and into a small room.

"Where are you from, Mrs Sehli?"

"I am originally from Glasgow, but my husband is from Saudi Arabia, hence my name."

"Oh, it sounds rather exotic."

"Yes it is," I smiled, "I have lived there, with all that sunshine, for 23 years."

"How lovely! Now Mrs Sehli, if you don't mind, would you please go behind the curtain, remove your top and put on this hospital gown, the doctor will be with you shortly."

I changed into the pastel blue gown and sat in one of the chairs beside a table. It was a brightly coloured room with soft colours of green, blues and yellows. A sink and mirror was positioned at one end of the of the room and a bed with matching coloured curtain screen at the other. The door handled turned and in walked a very pretty lady with a lovely smile, dressed casually but looking chic, with her maxi dress and gorgeous leather boots.

"Good Morning, Mrs Sehli, my name is Doctor Gillian."

"Hello Doctor Gillian, lovely to meet you," I said, feeling immediately at ease.

"I have read your notes from Doctor Muir. I am going to examine you now and then send you for a mammogram."

"Okay, thank you, doctor."

Doctor Gillian was so gentle and sympathetic during the examination.

"How have you been feeling these last few days, Mrs Sehli?"

"A bit sore and tender beside the lump, lethargic; feeling tired all the time, in fact, even falling asleep while I am sitting up."

"Okay Mrs Sehli, please get dressed and the nurse will show you where to go for your scan. When you are finished, please come back to me and we will discuss your results."

"Thank you, Doctor Gillian."

The machine for the mammogram looked quite harmless and delicate in soft pastel colours of pink and beige. Well you know what they say 'presentation is everything'. The x-ray for the right sided breast was easy, but the left side was so painful beside the lump. The radiographer was very professional and caring.

"I am sorry" she said as she placed my left breast between the two plates.

The pain became so intense.

"Please hurry," I pleaded.

"That's it, Mrs Sehli, it's over."

"Thank you, sorry for trying to rush you, it was just so painful on the lump side."

"Oh, you were fine, please don't worry. Now, after you change, go back to Doctor Gillian and I will send her the results as soon as possible."

I went back to the waiting room which has become quite busy, lots of things going on. I am feeling quite relaxed and there is still another hour until I meet up with mum.

"Mrs Sehli, would you please go back to the same room you were in this morning, Doctor Gillian is waiting for you."

That was quick, I thought, as I made my way to see Doctor Gillian.

"Hello again, Mrs Sehli, I have your mammogram results. They seem fine; however, due to the fact that you have quite dense tissue we need to do an ultrasound to get a clearer view."

"Oh," I said, trying to pretend that I wasn't worried.

"Please don't worry, Mrs Sehli, it's just a precaution."

Doctor Gillian showed me to the room for the ultrasound and introduced me to another doctor.

"When you finish, Mrs Sehli, please come back to my room and we will go over the results," said Dr Gillian.

I was left with the other doctor and she started the ultrasound.

"I am going to apply some gel while I scan. It will feel a little cold."

As the scan moved over me, I looked at the monitor, as lots of little x marks were appearing all over the screen. It was as if I was watching a version of Star Wars.

"Don't worry," said the doctor, "these ex's indicate benign cysts, so I will aspirate them."

"What does that mean?"

"Well, imagine your cysts are tiny balloons. I will insert a needle into them and they will disappear in front of you, so you will never have to worry."

"Is it going to be painful?"

"No, just a little nip."

As she started the procedure, it was a wee bit uncomfortable, but as she inserted the needle into each cyst they just disappeared from the screen as she had said.

"You see, Mrs Sehli, they are all benign and the procedure is over."

"Oh thank you," I said, "it's such a relief."

I will make an appointment to see you again in three months from now.

I was so relieved as I went back to see Doctor Gillian and give her the good news.

"This is great news, Mrs Sehli," said Doctor Gillian, "however, do you mind if I examine you once again?"

"Of course, Doctor".

As she touched the left side of my breast I wanted to cry with the pain.

"I am sorry Mrs Sehli, but I am not convinced with the ultrasound results. You are just too swollen and in too much pain. I will ask the doctor to repeat them and this time I will come inside with you. Let me go and check with the doctor and see if she can repeat the ultrasound now."

My heart missed a beat, gosh so much going on and even more worrying, I was going to be so very late for my meeting with mum. I looked at my watch, it's almost 1.00 pm, I need to call her.

"Hi mum it's Lesley, I am running a wee bit late."

"Are you okay, Lesley?"

"Yes mum, I am so sorry, I just got carried away with shopping in the West End."

"Don't worry, I will just order a coffee and relax with a newspaper till you get here."

"Thank you, mum, I won't be long."

Just at that moment Doctor Gillian returned, "Please come with me, Mrs Sehli. The doctor is waiting for us and we are going to repeat your ultrasound."

Doctor Gillian then asked the other doctor to move the scan over to where I felt the most pain, to where it was the most intense. I heard Doctor Gillian saying to the other Doctor.

"Look, there is a black shadow, there might be something there. I need to perform a biopsy."

When I heard this, I could feel my own heart pounding, Oh No, I thought, what was this Black Shadow?

"I am so sorry, Mrs Sehli, but I need to perform a cone biopsy to ensure that there is nothing untoward at the shadow location. Perhaps it is just another benign cyst."

"Is it a painful procedure, Doctor Gillian, and will it take a long time? It's just, I had an appointment five minutes ago?"

"Lesley, it won't take long and I will give you a local anaesthetic before I insert the needle to get the biopsy."

As Doctor Gillian explained the procedure and got ready to give me the local anaesthetic, a nurse entered the room and held my hand. The next thing I saw Dr Gillian holding, is only what I would have described as an electric drill, "Is that for me ???"

"Please, don't worry you will be alright. I am going to start now."

I looked away as the nurse held my hand tighter. I heard a faint clicking sound as the first needle went in. The second click and as the second needle went in, how it hurt. This time I was the one squeezing the poor nurse's hand.

"Are you okay?" asked Doctor Gillian?

I didn't want to appear a wimp, "A little sore," I groaned.

"I know, I am so sorry, but just one more and it will be all over."

As the third needle went in to my breast, my eyes began to swell.

"Please, no more, Doctor Gillian, I can't take any more!"

Doctor Gillian smiled kindly,

"It's alright Mrs Sehli. It's over. .... Just relax for a few moments. Would you like some water?"

"Yes, thank you, that would be nice."

"How are you feeling now?" she asked.

"I'm a wee bit tender."

"Oh yes, that's to be expected. You have been through a lot this morning. Please try not to worry, as I have told you, this is all just a precaution. I have made an appointment to see you again on Tuesday, after the weekend, as I will have your biopsy result by then."

"Thank you, Doctor, have a lovely weekend."

I left the room, with no more thoughts on the subject, as I rushed to hail a taxi. Luckily, the roads were quiet and within five minutes I had arrived at the book shop for lunch with mum.

"Hello mum," I said, as I approached her table, "I am sorry for being so late".

"It's okay" said mum, with her mischievous smile. "While I was waiting for you Lesley, I bought some beautiful Christmas cards. This is just such a beautiful shop."

We ordered lunch; delicious homemade lentil soup and a round of sandwiches.

"Your hair is beautiful mum."

"Thank you Lesley, I asked John to cut it quite short."

"So tell me, what's wrong Lesley?"

"Yes, you suit your hair short, mum."

"Now young lady, don't try to change the subject. What's wrong?"

"Nothing," I replied.

"But when you called me on the phone, you told me you forgot the time because you were so busy shopping."

"Yes mum, that's right."

"So Lesley, where is your shopping?"

I blushed, Oh No, she knows.

"I just didn't want to worry you mum. I was at the hospital for a wee check up as I haven't been feeling so well recently. It's probably nothing, just an infection, so I had a blood test and I will have the result next week."

"I see," she said, with her mischievous smile.

We said no more about it, but I saw the expression on her face, well, after all, I am her wee lassie. I think she knows, in fact I think we both know something isn't quite right, something is very wrong.

It feels like a long weekend, waiting for today to arrive and get my results. It's Tuesday and I am here at the hospital. It's rather early and the reception waiting area is not so busy. I take a seat and wait to be called. A young woman has just come out of one of the doctors' rooms, bless her, she has no hair. I wonder if it is the big C? Gosh, she looks like she is only in her thirties. Poor wee soul, I hope she will be okay. I must admit I am feeling a wee bit anxious, remembering the events that happened four days ago, which led me to being here today. I mean, let's face it, I seemed to have pulled the short straw, the fact that the ultrasound had detected a 'Black Shadow'. But, hey ho, onwards and upwards; today is 'D Day'.

"Mrs Sehli," I looked up as one of the nurses was smiling in my direction.

"This way please."

I followed her down the corridor and into the same wee room I had been in four days previously, where I first met Dr Gillian, my very own Miss Marple, who had discovered the black shadow. The nurse asked me kindly to take a seat,

"Doctor Gillian will be with you shortly Mrs Sehli."

"Thank you," I said, with a smile, as she left the room.

As I waited there was such a silence, except for the pounding of my own heart, as I waited for the doctor to walk through the door with my results. Two minutes later, I watched the handle of the door move as the door opened and Doctor Gillian walked in.

"Good Morning, Mrs Sehli, how are you today?"

"Good morning Doctor Gillian, I still feel quite tired and so very sore."

As Doctor Gillian sat down with me I asked her, "Am I okay?"

She looked at me tenderly "I am sorry, Lesley, we have found an abnormality."

I interrupted her quietly, "Do I have cancer?"

"Yes," she said, "we have found a tumour in your left breast."

I think only seconds passed before the door handle moved again and in walked another woman with a broad smile. "Good Morning, Mrs Sehli," she said, as she sat down, joining Doctor Gillian and I at the table. "I am Julie Doughty, your surgeon."

"My surgeon?" I said, rather surprised.

"Yes, please try not to worry Lesley, but as doctor Gillian will already have told you, we have found some abnormal cells in your left breast. It is an aggressive tumour and I need to operate as soon as possible, probably next week."

Again, I politely interrupted, "Am I going to die?"

She was specific yet kind as she said gently, "It is a rare cancer Lesley and very aggressive but at the moment your survival is 50/50. However, after your operation I will be able to give you a clearer diagnosis. Hopefully, we have caught it early and after treatment, you will make a full recovery."

As Miss Doughty continued speaking, the handle of the door moved again and in walked a woman wearing a smart suit. She had such a beautiful smile and portrayed an aura of empathy and calm. She stood quietly as my surgeon continued to explain what treatment plan I would be following over the months to come.

"After your operation Lesley you will probably have six months of chemotherapy, one month of radiotherapy, and one year of Herseptin which will be given intravenously. It is a new miracle drug and hopefully you will be a good match to receive it."

I remained calm and asked her the obvious question for a woman, "Will I lose my hair?"

"Yes," she said, "within three weeks, but," she whispered softly, "it will grow back. Now, before I examine you, let me introduce you to Jean, she is a nurse manager and will be with you for the next few years."

I cannot quite explain to you, but I felt so safe hearing these words, knowing that the woman with the beautiful aura would be my angel.

"Hello Lesley," she said.

"Hello Jean," I replied.

"Would you please come with me behind the screen and Miss Doughty will come and examine you?"

"Of course," I said, as I stood up and joined her behind the screen.

"Are you okay?" she asked me quietly.

"Yes," I replied, wishing it was all just a bad dream and that I would wake up at any moment.

After the examination, I got dressed, as my surgeon conferred with Doctor Gillian. As both doctors left the room, Doctor Gillian glanced back and said, "Try not to worry, Lesley, you are in good hands."

"Thank you," I said, as the door closed quietly behind them.

I turned to Jean, my eyes filled, I was trying to be so brave. She put her arms around me and promised,

"I will never leave you Lesley. You will never be alone."

I felt empowered not scared or sad, as though what had just happened had been perfectly orchestrated and timed. Three strangers were now going to play a very vital role in my survival. Jean and I chatted for a while as she gave me a copy of my treatment plan. I felt so comfortable with her, this stranger was about to become one of my best friends.

On leaving the hospital, I hailed a taxi and asked the driver to take me to Princess Square in Buchanan Street. Sitting in the taxi, my head was caught up in a whirlwind of emotions at the prospect of what was in front of me. So many wild thoughts were running through my mind, each clammering to be heard. All this was ahead of me and suddenly I thought, to hell with it. It was the Christmas season, made magical with all the beautiful twinkling lights and sparkling trees, covered in tinsel and baubles. There was a choir singing winter carols in the square and I was heading towards my favourite bistro where I would order a cheeseboard and a welcome glass of Pinot Grigio. I will put everything on the backburner and enjoy the moment. I'm calm. I will tell my husband tonight.

As Winston Churchill once said:

If you're going through hell, just keep going.

Three days later my letter arrived; my operation is 1st December. I am very sick, but I will survive.

My spirit is stronger than the black shadow.

Lesley A Sehli (1958 -   )

Note to Reader:

I have had a successful operation and have the result from the tumour biopsy. The good news is that the tumour has been removed. The not so good news is that it had already spread to my lymph nodes and I am Her2 positive which is aggressive and fast growing; however, I match up for the miracle drug that could save my life. My chemotherapy starts on 18th January. I am so going to enjoy this beautiful magical time called Christmas, before I start the fight for my life!

Lucky Girl

My big day has arrived. It's a cold, wet January morning, as my taxi drives along Glasgow's Great Western Road. I peer through the raindrops, running down the window, as I watch the hustle and bustle of a typical Monday morning rush. People scurrying around, trying not to bump into each other, negotiating round the puddles. Cars are beeping their horns, with lots of wee traffic jams along the way. I am not too bothered, it's only 8.00 a.m., and I have plenty of time as my appointment is not until 9.00 a.m. Cosying down in the back of the taxi I try relaxing to my Andrea Bocelli CD. Oh! how I love his music, particularly the song with Sarah Brightman, "Time to say Goodbye", although perhaps that is not so apt for today? On arriving at the beautifully designed and spacious building, I ask the driver to stop at the glass doors with the big sign 'Beatson Cancer Research.

"Thank you," I said, as I pay him the fare, with the customary £1 tip.

"Thank you, and Good Luck!" he said, as I left his cab.

I glanced back at him "Does he know? Does he know my secret?"

I walked through the entrance into a welcoming reception area with a cosy wee coffee shop on the side. I suppose as it is so early there are not many people around. It feels so very surreal thinking that within the next hour I will be having my first chemotherapy. Suddenly, I see a familiar face, thank goodness, it's Cathy, my chemotherapy nurse.

"Good Morning, Lesley," she says, as she greets me with a big smile and hug. "How are you?"

My heart is pounding, I can feel every beat, as I said, "I am fine, Cathy."

"It's okay, Lesley, you will be okay," she said, as she led me through another door and into a spacious, elegant room. How calming it is, with walls painted pastel yellow, ceiling cornices with strips of little lights gently changing colours, like that of a rainbow with its myriad hues, and music playing softly in the background. At the far end of the room, big windows look onto a little courtyard with a well-tended garden.

"This chair is for you Lesley," said Cathy, as I sat down on one of the big comfy chairs.

"Thank you," I said, as she hung my jacket on a hook at the back of the chair, then brought me some reading materials and offered me a tea or a coffee.

"Gosh, Cathy, I am so comfortable. I feel like I am sitting in a Health Spa," we laughed.

"I have a little questionnaire to run through with you, Lesley, before we start, so you just relax. I will get the paperwork and your coffee." As Cathy left the room, I heard a voice saying

"Hello there,"

"Hi," I said, looking over at a woman sitting on the other side of the room.

"I'm Sarah," she said, "What is your name?"

"Hello Sarah, my name is Lesley."

"So lovely to meet you Lesley," she said.

Sarah was extremely pretty, in her forties with auburn hair cut in to a stylish bob and the most beautiful emerald green eyes.

"So, you are the new kid on the block Lesley?"

"Yes, how do you know?" I said, looking at her with a surprised expression.

"Oh it's a dead giveaway; you still have your hair," she smiled.

"Well yes," I blurted out, "but you too, Sarah, have beautiful hair."

"Thank you," she smiled, "it's my latest wig. Isn't it amazing how real it looks?"

"Gosh," I said, "I thought it was your own hair Sarah. It looks so very real?"

"Oh Lesley, it is amazing nowadays. There are so many pretty choices, any colour, any style, any cut; you will see."

"Yes," I replied nervously.

"So Lesley, what's your prognosis?"

"Sorry?" I asked, taken aback at her question.

"Yes Lesley, I mean what type of cancer do you have?"

"Breast cancer, Sarah."

"Oh," she said, "have they caught it in time or has it spread?"

"It had spread to my lymph nodes, Sarah."

"Oh bugger," she replied "I am sorry about that."

"Oh," I said, "that's okay. They have removed all my affected nodes, so I hope it has been done in time."

"Oh I am sure," said Sarah, "fingers crossed Lesley. So what treatment plan have they given you?"

"They said I have to have everything, Sarah. Six months of chemotherapy, one month of radiotherapy and one year of a miracle drug called Herseptin which they said, luckily, I am a good match for."

"Oh, you are a Lucky Girl Lesley."

"What makes you say that, Sarah?" I asked.

"This miracle drug which they are going to give you, Herseptin, was only made available recently from America. It was a British woman who fought very hard for it to be available to women in this country. Unfortunately, it arrived to late to save her, indeed too late to save many of us, myself included."

For a few minutes I was struck dumb, but then I softly said

"There is something new coming out all the time, Sarah, new drugs keep appearing on the market."

She looked at me kindly,

"Oh yes Lesley, that is true, one must never give up hope."

Just at that moment Cathy returned with my cup of coffee and sat down beside me, explaining things and answering any questions and wee niggling doubts that I still might have. One of the big decisions I had to make this morning was regarding the Ice-Cap, an apparatus that can help minimise hair loss during chemotherapy. The cap is ice-cold and placed on your head for about one hour prior to the commencement of the chemotherapy. It does help some women, but for others it can leave them patchy, so I opted out, deciding, when the time was right, I would have my head shaved.

After this decision, Cathy walked to the other side of the room and returned with a trolley holding a bright yellow tray containing eight syringes; four coloured bright red and the remaining four with a clear liquid. Just at that moment, I couldn't believe it, his highness, my husband arrived in the room.

"This is my husband, Bassam."

"Hello Bassam, please have a seat. I am just about to begin with Lesley's chemotherapy."

As Cathy made some final preparations, I looked at him for support, but as usual, there wasn't any. He just stared at me with his darkly chilling eyes, as though I was a leper or one of the untouchables. Why had he even shown up? Sitting motionless, he put on his sunglasses, but his poker face could not be hidden from me anymore; he just didn't care.

"Bassam, why don't you just go? There is really nothing you can do here. Please, just come back to help me home in the evening. I will be finished around 6.00 p.m."

I was trying so hard to hold back my tears. It was so obvious he didn't love me. I think that I have known that for a long time, in fact, he really never did.

Grunting under his breath, he said, "Okay then, I will see you later," as he stood up and left.

I looked to Cathy, she was being so polite, pretending she hadn't noticed, but I knew in my heart that at least she would be there for me. My eyes focused back to the trolley with the syringes and needles.

"Is this all for me? Will it hurt Cathy?"

"No, I promise Lesley, it will be very quick. You won't even realise I have done it."

I looked away. I wanted to scream, but I didn't want to appear weak. I needed to be brave like Sarah and all those beautiful courageous women around me. As Cathy gently put the needle into my arm I felt a tiny sting, the cannula was attached. As the bright red fluid passed into my body, my eyes swelled, Cathy noticed the teardrop in my eye.

"Are you okay Lesley? What's wrong?"

"The red stuff, Cathy, is that what will take my hair away?"

"Yes Lesley, it is called Epirubicim, but look on the bright side; you won't have to shave your legs for six months."

Even at this point Cathy could still make me smile. Five minutes later, I was feeling a bit dizzy,

"I can see two of you, Cathy."

She squeezed my hand gently,

"Don't worry Lesley, put your head back. It will pass."

Putting my head back on the pillow, my eyes caught Sarah's from across the room. She smiled comfortingly as she whispered knowingly, "Keep strong, Lesley, you will be okay."

It's almost six in the evening, my first chemo is over. I am feeling fine, just a wee bit tired.

"Here is a bag of medication, Lesley," said Cathy, "the district nurses will come to your house and administer you daily injections for the first week after every chemotherapy session, to build up your immune system and remember Lesley," she said with a naughty smile "all the red stuff in the syringes, well don't panic tonight because you will be peeing red BIG time!"

"Okay," I said, as we both roared with laughter!

I bid goodnight to Sarah and all those other courageous women whom I had met this eventful day. My first chemo is over, my journey has begun, yes, as Sarah said: "I am a 'Lucky Girl'".

"I felt sorry for myself because I had no shoes, until I met a man who had no feet"

(Jewish Proverb)

Mirror, Mirror, On The Wall

The two district nurses, Claire and Margaret, from Doctor Muir's clinic, have popped in today to start my daily injections. As I make coffee, we chat and I feel thoroughly relaxed.

"You have a beautiful home, Lesley."

"Thank you."

"It so big. How many rooms do you have?"

"Well, all together between the Penthouse at the top and this one, we have five bedrooms, three of which are en suite and, of course, dining rooms, lounges and open plan kitchens."

"It really is so lovely. You must enjoy living here?"

I only nodded, thinking if she only knew.

"How are you feeling after your first chemo, Lesley?"

"Oh fine, thank you ladies, the wee bit of nausea I was feeling seems to have gone, probably because of the medication I have been prescribed."

"Are you alone at home, Lesley?"

"No my husband is here but he has a business meeting today. In fact, after my injection I too have a meeting, with my mum this afternoon, as we have an appointment at Maggie's, The Cancer Care Centre. I need to buy some pretty scarves and pick up any tips that might make my journey a wee bit easier."

"Oh yes, it is a great place to go, the people are so kind and you will feel so relaxed the minute you walk through the door," said Claire.

"This is what I have heard from many of the other women who I met at my chemo."

"Now, young lady," said Margaret, as she prepared and sterilized the area, "are you ready?"

"Yes, Margaret."

I turned away as she gently administered the injection into my tummy.

"Are you okay Lesley?"

"Yes, thank you."

"Just relax, deep breath, it will be over soon."

"Okay, done!"

Oh my goodness, I couldn't believe it. I felt nothing. It was all over in a flash!

"Well done Lesley, see you don't have to worry. This procedure is going to build up your immune system."

"Oh great, thank you so much ladies. You have been so kind."

"You are welcome, Lesley, we are off now to our next patient and we will see you again tomorrow."

That afternoon, as mum and I approached Maggie's we are so amazed at the glass building and its beauty through design. It has a Scandinavian look with a James Bond twist, set within the Beatson Hospital grounds amongst luscious green grass, trees and flowers. It was my lovely nurse Jean who told me about Maggie's.

"Gosh, isn't it beautiful," said mum, as we enter through the glass sliding doors, to where one feels immediately an aura of calm. Throughout the open space are very comfortable sofas, chairs and pretty flowers in vases. We are met by a welcoming lady, one of the many volunteers who asks us kindly to take a seat with an offer of tea, coffee and biscuits. Indeed, just as my district nurse Claire had said, 'a home from home'.

"I will just let the hairdresser know you are here, Mrs Sehli."

"Thank you."

I felt so relaxed, as did mum. It is such an empowering place. We could hear the laughter of people attending different support groups and others just there for a good natter. A few minutes later an elegant woman approached mum and I.

"Hello Mrs Sehli, my name is Sharon."

"Hello Sharon, please just call me Lesley, and this is my mum, May."

"Hello May, would you like to follow me through ladies, to the hair salon?"

Mum and I followed Sharon through to her spacious salon called 'Talking Heads'.

"How can I help you, Lesley?"

"I have just had my first chemo and need to prepare myself for when I lose my hair. My nurse Jean told me all about you, Sharon, and the good work you do."

"Thank you, Lesley."

"In fact while mum and I were sitting outside we both commented on the beautiful scarves some of the women are wearing. Could you help me please with some ideas Sharon?"

"Of course Lesley, if you sit on this seat here, beside the mirror, I will help you to choose some pretty scarves and we can practice together some beautiful styles."

Sharon arranged another coffee for mum and then what fun we had as she brought out an array of beautiful scarves to choose from. Mum and I had been a wee bit apprehensive at first, but there had been no need.

We had a wonderful afternoon with Sharon. I chose one scarf blue, the other yellow. Mum chose for me a pastel pink with a rose, which would become my favourite and which I would choose to wear most of the time. Being at Maggie's is a haven where you feel relaxed, happy and safe. Like having someone put their arm around you and say: "You are not alone, I am here to help." And that is so true!

It's only three days till my next chemo and I am feeling great. My only real sadness and aggravation is Bassam. My being ill has not enticed him to be any more kind to me, in fact the opposite. So much verbal and emotional abuse, it is becoming much worse. I cannot tell people, especially mum, it would break her heart, somehow I just have to manage him until I am stronger. These last few weeks he has not been getting back home until late and that is, if he comes home at all, after spending all night at the casino until around 6.00 a.m. or 7.00 a.m. I swear Monsieur Cancer is easier to have as a friend than this man whom I have married. I have spoken with my brother in law, Talal, in Saudi Arabia, who says he will help me but has still done nothing.

I am so looking forward to today as my best friend Jenny has arrived from London for a few days holiday, visiting her parents. I am sure today will be a day for catch up and lots of fun. My girlie friends all enjoy my cooking and today I have planned a Malaysian feast of prawns in sambal with lime leaves, seabass in coconut, okra in oyster on a bed of noodles, watered down with fresh mango juice. Living with a gambler, your life is sometimes feast or sometimes famine. Jenny arrives, as usual, laden with flowers, wine and chocolate. We sit at the table over lunch and chatter with endless laughter.

"How good is this?" says Jenny, catching one of the prawns with her chopstick. "So, how are you feeling, Lesley? You do look great and your hair is looking quite thick and in great condition?"

"Thank you," I said, as I got up and looked in the gilded mirror above the fireplace. "I have only three days left until my second chemo, perhaps I am going to prove them wrong and still have my hair? By the way, I had a great time with mum at Maggie's and have bought some beautiful scarves."

"Let me see," said Jenny.

"How fabulous," she said, as we had our own wee fashion show, dancing around the room through a rainbow of scarves. Such fun, madness, a real chilled out day!

That very same evening, as I got ready for bed, little clumps of hair started to come away in my brush. I quietly went through to my private bathroom with it's very high ceilings adorned with mosaic and marble columns. A huge, ornate, gold-gilded mirror hung over my gold-rimmed, antique vase, which had been a gift from my parents for my 21st birthday. Sweet scented pink blossoms filled the air. Although Bassam gave me the minimum of money to run the house, I always tried to have enough to buy fresh flowers for my own pleasure.

"Why don't you just buy plastic flowers?" he would say, "they last longer."

My creams were arranged on the left side of the gilded mirror and my perfumes on the right. As I picked up my brush and gently started to brush my hair little clumps started to fall away. Oh my, I thought the time has come! My eyes slowly moved back to the mirror, I put my brush down and carefully moved my fingers through my hair. Little threads, like those taken from a spider's web, came away on my fingers and fell to the floor. Cathy was right. I would lose my hair before my second chemo. I felt a wee bit sad, but not for long, as I realised this was just part of the process and my hair would soon grow back. I quietly went back to my bedroom, placing my new pink scarf with the rose, the one that mum had chosen, under my pillow. As I lay my head gently down, I closed my eyes, drifting off to sleep realising that tomorrow would be another big day, but with the knowledge that I was ready for whatever might be.

It's six o'clock in the morning, I have tossed and turned all night. I had better get up, I just can't sleep. As I lift my head, I can see that some more of my hair has fallen during the night and is now lying on my pillow. Bassam doesn't keep many promises, but he did say he would shave my head when it was the right time. I will wake him up in a couple of hours to help me, if he has actually come home?

He must be back; his keys are on the hallway table. He sleeps alone in the master bedroom, not with me anymore. He says that I am looking ugly and he can't sleep for the noise of the fan. I have the fan because of being too hot during the night. It is one of the side effects from the chemo. He has no empathy whatsoever. To be honest with you, it's better he is not with me. The less I see of him the better!

It's almost 10.00 a.m. and I am ready for my new trendy hair style, yes the new Gi Jane, well let's face it if Demi Moore looked cool, then why shouldn't I? In my bathroom, I have prepared a comfy chair in front of my gilded mirror, with a towel and box of tissues. Andrea Bocelli's music plays softly in the background while I pour myself a large glass of Merlot. I realise it is only 10.00 a.m., but I want to do this in style.

It's time to wake up Bassam. Opening the master bedroom door quietly, I whisper gently, "Good morning Bassam," but there is no answer, again nervously but a bit louder, I say "Good Morning Bassam."

He groans and looks up from the duvet with a mumbled, "What is it? What do you want?"

"I have made you some tea Bassam."

"I don't want it now. I am tired. Leave me alone."

"But please, Bassam, I need you to get up, my hair is falling and you promised to shave my head when it was time?"

"You are nothing but a nuisance," he shouted.

I ignored his hurtful remark and once again, this time I had to plead, "Please, help me."

"Alright," he blurted out, "I will get up in five minutes."

I waited another thirty minutes, butterflies in my stomach and still no Bassam. He really is impossible. I think it is obvious for everyone to see that he couldn't care less what happens to me. Almost an hour later he appears. Sitting in my seat in front of the mirror with my wee pink scarf on my lap, I take a sip of wine as I listen to the shaver being switched on. I close my eyes so as to concentrate not on the shaver but on the soft melodies of Bocelli playing in the background. As Bassam moves the shaver over my head, I can feel little fluffy bits of hair falling on to my face, back of my neck and then gently resting on to the back of my hands which preciously guards my wee pink scarf. I am not going to open my eyes, but I just hope that Bassam won't hate me any more than he already does' with my wee bald head about to be revealed. The shaver stopped, it was over, the deed was done as Bassam left me alone with my thoughts. Still not daring to look in the mirror, I took a long hot shower. It felt so calming and refreshing. I felt so clean and gradually brave enough to touch my head. It was such a weird feeling to be so smooth, yet I felt so empowered and brave. Still not yet daring to look in the mirror, I got dressed and placed my scarf on my head, just as Sharon had shown me in Maggie's. My scarf felt secure, my heart was pounding as I opened my eyes and looked in the mirror. I am not yet brave enough to look at my bald head.

Wow, I thought, how chic am I?

Picking up my wine glass, I toast myself in the mirror. "Well done Lesley."

As I opened the door to leave the room I turned back to the mirror, for a final glimpse.

"Mirror, Mirror on the Wall, Who now is The Fairest of them All?"
My reflection kindly smiled back!

'You can't be brave if you've only had
Wonderful things happen to you!'
Mary Tyler Moore

Cupid

Today's my second chemo. The oncology receptionists Isabelle and Anne are always so friendly and welcoming with the most delicious box of chocolates sitting beside them for us ladies to demolish while sipping coffee, chatting, laughing and supporting each other when need be, as we are all on a similar journey. There is a selection of magazines, a TV monitor to catch up on the day's events and a wee water font which gurgles happily in the corner. My name is called, as the nurse politely shows me through to the bay and my chair.

"Oh, what a pretty scarf," I hear, turning round and seeing none other than the familiar face of Sarah. There is such a strong support between all of us. Such brave women I am meeting, so upbeat and inspirational. Cathy, my beautiful nurse approaches, "Good Morning, Lesley, I hear you have had a good three weeks."

"Yes, thank you, Cathy."

"Are you ready for today?"

"Oh yes," I said, "but Cathy, yesterday it was quite painful getting the needle in my arm, to take blood. Some women I noticed prefer the needle in their hand, may I try it that way?"

"Of course, Lesley, I will find a big juicy vein there and use some Emla baby cream to numb the area, so you won't feel a thing."

"Thank you, Cathy."

Pat, the volunteer, has arrived with her trolley of goodies: a variety of freshly made sandwiches, fruits, yogurts and juice. She is very much one of those invaluable people, who spend a big part of their life looking after people like me. Relaxing with our refreshments, we ladies chat and discuss the world, the latest fashion trends and our own plans for when we get better, a relaxing vacation being top of the list. I have to say it is so uplifting here, I actually forgot this morning for a wee while, why I am here. I forget how sick I am. It's almost 3.00 p.m. in the afternoon and the second Chemo is over. Bassam said he would pick me up, but he is still not here. I have been waiting one hour in the waiting room and I am starting to feel quite tired. If he doesn't show up soon, I will have to call a taxi. Five minutes later my mobile rings. It's Bassam

"I am here, outside in the parking, hurry up I can't wait. I have a meeting tonight at Gleneagles," he says, as he hangs up the phone.

It really doesn't matter any more how he treats me. I feel so humbled and so very special because of Cathy and all the nursing team. Today I have been showered with so much love, enough to last me for the next three weeks, until I come back for chemo number three!

Four days have passed. When I woke up this morning I couldn't believe it as I looked in the mirror as to how different I was looking. As I got closer to the mirror I soon realised that I have no eyebrows. Goodness I thought, I must have moulted during the night. Looks like it is going to be one of those days.

I mean, "What's a girl to do?" ….. "Just carry on I suppose!"

Claire and Margaret have arrived for my daily injections and after they leave I am going wig shopping with mum.

"Have you any plans for Valentine's day?" asks Claire.

"Not yet, but hopefully Bassam will plan something nice and I will probably cook one of his favourite meals."

"Your husband must be so busy, Lesley, we were looking forward to meeting him."

"Oh yes he has so much business, (monkey business I thought to myself) I too, hardly ever see him."

"Are you okay though, Lesley, spending so much time on your own?"

"Oh yes, my mum and my friends keep an eye on me and if ever I was feeling a wee bit unwell then I can call them at any time. Thankfully, at the moment, I am feeling fine."

Mum and I are on our way to the hair salon. It's a ten-minute walk from my penthouse to the specialised wig salon called Enhance Hair Solutions. Mum and I are met by a friendly receptionist, called Melissa.

"Hello, I am Mrs Sehli, and I have an appointment for a wig fitting."

"Oh yes ladies, if you would like to follow me through, Lyn is waiting for you".

Lyn was lovely and welcoming, "Hello Mrs Sehli, please ladies have a seat and make yourselves comfortable. May I offer you a tea or coffee?"

What a lovely welcome, mum and I thought, as we surveyed our surroundings. The room was pleasing and relaxing, just like a mini hair salon, with wash basins, mirrors, hair dryers and shelves with neatly arranged towels and hair products. As Melissa brought our coffees, Lyn sat with us, describing and showing us the many different styles and colours of wigs she had.

"What style did you have in mind, Lesley?"

"I think golden blonde and shoulder length, something that I can wear up or down."

"Okay," she said, "Let me go and bring some samples for you to try."

"Mum, I am a wee bit shy, I haven't looked at my wee bald head yet?"

"What?" she said, rather surprised.

"Well from the minute my head was shaved, I never looked in the mirror until I had my scarf on my head, I even sleep with it on."

Mum smiled gently, "Lesley you are beautiful and always will be, just remember it's what's inside that counts."

"You are right mum. Do you want to be here while I remove my scarf?"

"Oh Lesley don't be silly, of course I will, you are my wee lassie."

Lyn and Melissa returned with a wonderful selection of wigs to try on and choose from. Sarah was right, so many styles and colours. I was spoiled for choice.

"Let me help you," said mum, as she gently unfolded my scarf. My wee bald head was revealed, I looked at mum but she was taking it all in her stride.

"Gosh, I actually do look quite cool. What a drama Queen am I?"

"Absolutely," said mum, with her mischievous smile.

After some time, I had made my choice. I feel like a new woman with my new golden bob. As we left the salon I tucked my wee pink scarf into my bag. Beaming with confidence, mum and I decided to go for a well-deserved, afternoon cream-tea. The perfect ending to a perfect day! Thank you Mum!

Loving A Child Doesn't Mean Giving In To All His Whims;
To Love Him Is To Bring Out The Best In Him,
To Teach Him To Love
What Is Difficult '
(Nadia Boulanger)

Gosh already second week after my last chemo, I am feeling quite sick and drained. Tomorrow is Valentine's Day, I don't think Bassam has planned anything, but that's okay, because if I am feeling like this tomorrow I am just going to put my wee head under the duvet.

It's Valentine's Day, Bassam is still not around. I am feeling quite nauseous, perhaps after a shower and my medication I will feel better. Goodness, in the mirror, I am looking so drained, whatever could be happening? I will just take it easy today and tonight I will put on some of my new lipstick from the Body Shop to perk myself up. At 5.00 p.m. the phone rings. It's Bassam.

"Hi Lesley, didn't get home last night because I had a meeting up in Perth. I am on my way home now, so I should be there around 7.00 p.m. Can you prepare some dinner?"

This man is going to be the death of me if I am not careful. What did I ever see in him? I keep telling myself to stay strong, deal with Monsieur Cancer and then I will be able to deal with him. It's 6.00 p.m. I am feeling a bit better but I still look drained. Tonight, I am wearing my lovely red silk dress, but even after applying my new lip gloss and mascara it doesn't seem to have made such a difference. What's happening? Oh no, please, not tonight. Can you believe it? I've got no eyelashes! This is awful, of all days for this to happen. Never mind, I will call Jenny. She will cheer me up and make me laugh.

"Hi Jenny, how are you? Happy Valentine's."

"And to you Lesley, how are you?"

"You will never believe it Jenny; I have just lost my eyelashes."

"Lesley, it's okay, we knew this would happen, it's all part of the process. I know it is not easy but you are so brave, please stay strong."

"Yes, I don't want to appear a wous, it's just everything seems to be happening so quickly."

"You are not a wous Lesley, you are the bravest and most positive woman I know and don't you ever forget that. Is Bassam not there?"

"No, but he said he was coming home in time for dinner so I have marinated some salmon, but you know, seeing is believing with him."

"Oh, you shouldn't bother, you are not well. He should be there to help you."

"I know Jenny, but you know the situation. I just want to get better, get my life back and everything he has taken from me."

"Has he hit you Lesley?"

"Yes, the other day he grabbed me by the back of my neck and pushed me through the door."

"Oh Lesley, you should have called the police."

"No Jenny, I have my dignity, and really, I am okay."

"Lesley, please, if he ever hurts you again, I need you to call me, please promise me that."

"I promise Jenny but I don't want you to tell anyone else?"

"Okay, Lesley, but I am not happy about this. I will call you every day, please try not to stress over him, just concentrate on you, and once this treatment is over you will get your life back."

"Thanks Jenny, you are right; onwards and upwards. I will call you tomorrow."

"Okay and please remember you can call me anytime day or night."

"Thank you Jenny, Goodnight".

It's 8.00 p.m. and Bassam is still not here. I am all dressed up and nowhere to go. At around 9.00 p.m. he eventually comes through the door, "These are for you," he says, as he hands me a bunch of multi-coloured tulips, from the local gas station.

"Thank you," I said, as I arranged them in my grandmother's crystal vase. "It's quite late Bassam, was your journey okay?" I said trying hard to make him think, as usual, I still believed his stories.

"Yes, I had a detour to my friend Ali's house as his wife insisted I have dinner with them."

"But I have prepared dinner for us, it's Valentine's Day, Bassam."

"So, we can have it tomorrow. I am not hungry now."

"Bassam, you are impossible, I am feeling tired. I am off to bed, see you later."

I left him in the lounge talking on one of his many mobiles. In the bedroom I turned on the TV to try and relax. Goodness, forget losing my eyebrows, he hadn't even noticed my red silk dress. For the next two hours I didn't sleep all I could do was toss and turn. I think I will get up and make myself a soothing cup of camomile tea. As I opened the bedroom door, the hallway was dark and although the lights were off in the lounge I could hear someone talking. As I quietly crept along the long hallway and approached the door of the lounge I couldn't believe what I was hearing. My heart was thumping in my chest. Bassam was sitting in the dark, on his mobile, talking with another woman.

"Yes, I want to meet you. Well let's meet and take it from there. I am sure you will enjoy my company as I will yours. We will have a great time together. Well, yes, I am married, but she is not a problem. I don't think she will last much longer; she is terminally ill with cancer. Good, so I will see you tomorrow night. We will have dinner and then take it from there. Goodnight Darling."

I opened the door, "Who is she Bassam?"

"F….off" he said.

"Why are you doing this to me? You know I am ill, but I am not terminal. Why are you hurting me? Who is she?"

"Shut up," he said, "Why don't you just die? You are such a bad investment."

Trembling, I took the flowers from the vase and threw them at him, "You are evil, Bassam."

Standing up and turning, with eyes of ice, he pushed me through the door to the hallway and glancing back he said, "Woman, you are finished, you don't have long to go."

He opened the door and banged it closed behind him as he went to the private elevator.

Sitting in the dark, motionless, I cried myself to sleep.

Cupid shot an arrow, he shot it very high,
It missed my heart completely
When he told me Die!

I have just got home from my third chemo. It didn't go as well as usual. I took a small turn as the chemo started. Seemingly my veins are collapsing which made it quite a painful process so it had to be stopped. A doctor was called but after a wee rest, the chemo was re-booted but using my other arm. I have now been scheduled on the morning of my fourth chemo for a procedure where, under sedation, a surgeon will insert a Hickman Line from my jugular vein, which will exit from my chest wall. Cathy has told that it is not a difficult or painful procedure, just a wee bit uncomfortable for a few minutes. However, she has said that it that it will make the administering of my chemo really easy and looking on the bright side I am okay about it as it will mean 'no more needles', Yippee.

***

Three weeks have passed, I am okay but feeling very tired and quite drained. My walking is now very slow and I need to take the lift to get to the lower penthouse, on the second floor. The VIP that was renting the top penthouse from us has left to return to Spain and Bassam is spending most of his time up there. Goodness knows what he gets up to? He keeps telling me to stop the chemo treatment, even though he knows that the cancer I have is very aggressive and I might not survive without it.

"I don't want to die, Bassam?"

"Grow up," he answered, "we all have to die sometime."

Well, today is the big day for the fourth chemo and my Hickman Line to be fitted. I have insisted that Bassam takes me as I cannot go it alone.

On entering the Procedure Room, for the line to be fitted, I am met by the surgeon. "Don't worry Mrs Sehli," she said, "it is a short procedure."

Lying on the table I was given a local anaesthetic as the nurse gently held my hand. I was feeling relaxed but it was so uncomfortable as the surgeon made the incision and then started to feed the line through to my chest wall. "It will be over soon," said the surgeon, as I started to squeeze the nurse's hand, she smiled. "It's okay, Lesley, you are okay. It will be over soon."

Fifteen minutes later and thank goodness, it was over. I rested for five minutes and then the nurse called Bassam to help and take me to the other side of the hospital where they were waiting for me with Chemo four. Bassam dropped me off at the Oncology building.

"What time shall I pick you up?" he asked.

"It's okay, Bassam, I will take a taxi home you just go on for your evening appointment."

I would rather take a taxi than sit waiting one or two hours for him to arrive. It's really not funny anymore, he is always arriving late and I am just too poorly at the moment to put up with anymore of his antics.

"Hello," said Cathy, who was waiting for me with another of the nursing team, called Donna.

"Hello ladies," I said, feeling so happy to meet up with them. Even though I was going to have chemo, I knew that for the rest of the afternoon the people here would show me nothing but kindness. As though being wrapped in a wee bit of cotton wool, even if only for a couple of hours. Please don't think I am looking for pity, absolutely not, but I am quite sick as you know and a little bit of caring from these beautiful nurses help me to feel loved and safe. This is not a cheesy statement, but the truth. They don't know the abuse I am going through at home, no one does but Jenny, and for now it has to stay this way until I am stronger.

"Right then, Lesley, let's get you seated on a comfy chair and prepare you for your next chemo. Now you have this line inserted it will make things so much easier for you."

"Goodness, Cathy, can you believe it, I am half way through my chemotherapy treatment and only have another three months to go?"

"I know, Lesley, and you are doing so well."

My chemo started, and yes, as Cathy had said it was so easy with the Hickman Line and not a needle in sight.

"Lesley, did you have lunch?" asked Donna.

"No, not yet" I replied.

"Well, why don't you have a nap and I will ask Pat to pop by shortly with her trolley?"

"Oh yes, that would be wonderful, thank you Donna."

Sure enough Pat arrived. "What would you like today, Lesley? I have some delicious sandwiches."

"Oh, thank you Pat, the tuna would be lovely, with a black coffee."

I relaxed with my lunch and then called mum. "Hi mum. I was thinking of staying with you tonight."

"Oh great Lesley, your room is ready and the kettle will be on."

My day at the hospital is over. I got a taxi to mum and dad's. Aunt Helen, popped round to visit. We had a delicious dinner together. I feel happy and relaxed knowing that I am in the company of those that love me.

Two weeks pass, I haven't gone out too much except to go and see mum to enjoy sitting with her, relaxing in the garden. She has that mischievous smile whenever she asks me about Bassam, but I don't tell her too much because I don't want her to worry. I know she frets when she sees me like, this, fighting for my life, but I do always try to be strong in front of her. The other day Bassam took me out for dinner, I pushed myself to go with him, but all the way in the car he just commented on my swelling body and how ugly my neck looked with this Hickman Line and that I should cover up with a polo neck sweater to hide it. At dinner that night, I suggested that since he didn't seem to have any feelings for me anymore, then perhaps the way forward would be a divorce.

"We can go to a lawyer Bassam and just split the property between us and then go our separate ways?"

"Oh no, Lesley, I do care for you. I just have so much on my mind and if in future we ever did divorce, I would always make sure that you will be comfortable. If I die all my shares in Saudi Arabia, from the lands and family business will go to you, as my wife and next of kin."

I smiled gently, knowing that this like everything else would be a lie and I knew that, as he spoke, he was up to something behind my back. I knew it wouldn't be good but I am just too weak at this point to do anything about it.

Going for my fifth chemo today, but yesterday at the clinic I told one of the lovely nurses Miriam that I am feeling so very weak and my heart is continually palpitating.

"Yes Lesley, I think you are looking a little anaemic. We will have to do some tests."

My blood count is low and tomorrow before my chemo five, they are preparing me for a blood transfusion.

Oh dear, I am not feeling well at all.

After the transfusion I got a taxi home and fell into bed. Yet again, there is no food in the fridge but I am just too tired. I need to sleep; tomorrow is another big day.

It's the day after my transfusion and fifth chemo, I have to say I am feeling better and a bit stronger after the blood transfusion, but I will be so very happy when this treatment is over another three weeks and counting.

Time goes by so quickly, only three days now until my final chemo. I am so trying to be strong, but I am not feeling so well at all since last week. My walking is terrible and I am so fatigued. I walked over to Marks & Spencer about a ten-minute walk away from the penthouse and bought some groceries for a few days with my visa card. Goodness knows how I am going to settle the bill when it comes in. Beg Bassam, I suppose, it's all about survival at the moment. I am spending most of the time in bed. Mum and Jenny call me every day, but I am even too tired to have a full conversation.

"Shall I come over?" says mum.

"No, really, it's okay mum, I just need lots of sleep. I promise I will come over tomorrow."

"Super Lesley, tomorrow we can relax together in the garden. I will prepare the parasol. They say it is going to be another sunny day."

I wish I could tell mum the truth about Bassam, but I can't. I have told her a wee white lie, that Bassam is home every evening preparing meals and looking after me. I need to protect her, she is older now and takes petit mal seizures, it would cause her too much stress if she knew the truth. What else can I do? I love her so much. As you are reading this I hope you realise, although my body is failing my brain certainly isn't. If I leave Bassam at this point, I will never get my rights as a wife, he might disappear into oblivion taking everything and leaving me with nothing. I believe this is the way his brain is now working. If I die he will have won, taking everything I have worked so hard for, having tormented me with both verbal and physical abuse, for which there would never be justice.

The following day was lovely spent with mum. We had lunch, chatted and laughed as mum took us down memory lane sharing stories of when she was a lass. As the sun began to set we both were feeling so relaxed, closing our eyes under the parasol as a gentle breeze cradled us in love. That same evening when I returned home, to my disbelief and horror I noticed that my jewellery box was open and my Chopard diamond watch and diamond necklace, my gifts from King Fahad, were missing. Bassam as usual is not answering his mobile and he is the only one who has access to my jewellery box. Just before midnight he arrives home.

"Bassam, did you remove my Chopard diamond set from my jewellery box?"

"Oh, here we go," he said, "complaining as usual."

"What complaining Bassam, either you have my jewellery and I am asking you why or I have been robbed and I need to call the police."

His demeanour changed the minute I mentioned the word police. He quickly reciprocated,

"You don't understand, I met my friend who is a jeweller, this afternoon at the shooting range, and he wanted to borrow it for a display at a jewellery event."

"What? You have no right to do that. How dare you? Please get it back from him first thing tomorrow."

"I can't he is travelling round the country."

I knew he was lying. "I don't believe you. I don't believe anything you say anymore. All you ever do is lie."

"Oh shut up you are nothing but a f----bitch."

"Please don't talk like this to me anymore. I think you have sold my jewellery for your gambling and women. I have had enough, please get my jewellery back or I will call your brother, Talal, in Saudi Arabia and tell him what you are doing to me."

"Shut up, you bitch, you are out of this house."

"That suits me, as soon as we see a lawyer and a settlement is agreed."

He was furious, his eyes so black and cold, cutting through my very being. I sensed he was losing the plot and I knew that at any moment I was about to feel his wrath. He slapped my face as I tried to turn away, he caught me by the back of my wee pink scarf, kicked and pushed me to the other side of the room. I slid along the oak floor, falling and banging my head at the side of the big, stone dining table.

I screamed, "Leave me alone or I will call the police."

"Call them, you sharmouta! You are bipolar and the chemotherapy has affected your brain."

"You are evil, Bassam. I am going to get a lawyer."

He picked up his keys from the hallway and before he left, turned back and said, "Get a lawyer, it's all my money. You are getting nothing. I found you on the street and you are going back to the street. Go and get a job as a maid. That is all you are good for." Then, leaving the penthouse, he slammed the door behind him.

Still on the floor, I sat quietly, too weak to move, too exhausted to cry. I felt for my Hickman Line, so worried that it had been dislodged, knowing full well, that if that was the case I would be in real trouble, but thank goodness, I am still attached. My head is pounding, my face is hurting, but my spirit will not be broken!

It is better to die on your feet, than to live on your knees.
(Dolores Ibarruri)

Final chemo today, thank goodness. I just need to get through.

"How are you today?" asked Cathy.

"Sorry, I don't want to moan Cathy, but I really feel sore, all over. My walking is terrible and I seem to have developed a cough."

"Are you getting enough rest, Lesley?"

"Yes, I just have a lot of things on my mind, but I will be fine."

"Lesley, I am here anytime you want to talk and remember, you are going through a lot."

"Oh, I know, thank you."

"Today, is now your last chemo, and it will be over," she said, hugging me. "You have done so very well!"

Thank goodness I got through the day. Next month I will start 31 days of radiotherapy, and, hopefully, soon I will start to get better.

It's a week since my last chemo, my coughing has become worse and I am being sick. Margaret and Claire, the district nurses, have told me to see Doctor Muir if I get any worse. My wee body is in so much pain, but I must keep strong because I know it is all part of the process and I will have to get more sick with the treatment before I get better. So, hopefully, onwards and upwards!

Two weeks have passed and tomorrow I am going to the hospital for a check-up. The woman in the mirror isn't me anymore. I can hardly recognise her. I am swollen from head to toe and my eyes are actually bleeding blood. I am coughing all the time and can hardly catch my breath. I think something isn't quite right. I called my oncology nurse, Jean, for advice. She has been so lovely calling me regularly during these six months and has made me feel uplifted on the days that I feel like crap.

"Lesley, don't worry but I want you to go to the oncology clinic at the hospital first thing tomorrow morning You are not sounding so well. I think you might have an infection and need some antibiotics."

"Okay Jean, I will. By the way, would it be okay if I meet up with you sometime next week? I need a little advice. It is of a personal nature, regarding my husband."

"Of course, Lesley, you just tell me when and I will make myself free."

"Thank you, Jean," I said, as I tried to catch a breath.

"Now Lesley, get some fluids in you and get to bed. You have all my numbers. Please remember you can call me anytime, but you must go to the clinic first thing tomorrow morning."

"Okay, I will. Thank you, Jean."

As I hung up the phone, my only thoughts were of my fighting to survive and dealing with Bassam's abuse. Because of what he is doing to me, it might affect my chances of survival, that's why I have decided to talk to Jean!

Next morning, I arrived at the oncology clinic. Bassam had to bring me to the clinic as it is obvious I am in a terrible way. There are quite a few people waiting as I take a seat. A nurse, who I have seen before at the clinic, approaches me.

"Hello, Mrs Sehli, how are you?"

"Hello, I am actually not feeling so well and I am finding it difficult to breathe."

"You just relax, Mrs Sehli, and we will get a doctor to see you as soon as possible."

I turned to Bassam, "I can't breathe."

"Well you should have come to the hospital before now."

"Please Bassam, stop fighting with me."

A couple of minutes later the nurse approached me again,

"Mrs Sehli, rather than waiting here, there is a room over there with a single bed, how about I take you over there? It will be more comfortable for you while you are waiting to see the doctor."

It sounded like manna from heaven.

"Oh yes, that would be fine," I said slowly, feeling my energy ebb away.

A nursing auxiliary, in a green uniform, came over to help her take me to the room, while Bassam followed. No sooner was I in the room than the door shut and a team of doctors and nurses were already waiting there with lots of equipment. Eventually I would realise this was a 'set up', yes a 'set up' that would hopefully save my life. The medical staff had already realised how seriously ill I was. My temperature was too high; my pulse was erratic. I was plugged up to machines and drips. "Don't worry, Mrs Sehli," said the auxiliary. I wasn't sure what was happening but I could see at the other side, in the corner of the room Bassam sitting, watching and saying nothing.

"What's wrong with me?" I asked.

"We are not sure, Mrs Sehli. We are trying to stabilize you and then you will be able to breathe more easily."

It was a scary time, but I knew, once again, my life was in good hands. After some time, I was stabilised.

"Mrs Sehli, I am one of the oncology doctors. You are now stable but we have to do some tests to find out what is going on. Have you anyone with you?"

"Yes, that's my husband, Bassam, over there."

"Hello Mr Bassam, your wife at the moment is stable but we will have to keep her in the hospital, to find out what is going on. We are arranging a room for her and at the moment we will keep her here until we feel that she can be moved."

"Thank you, Doctor," I could hear him say.

As the medical team left the room I was left with Bassam, sitting at the other side of the room, with the bleep of various monitors. I was so exhausted.

"Bassam," I said, trying to catch a breath, "please let mum and dad know where I am."

My eyes were closing but I could sense him approaching my bed. He bent over and whispered in my ear,

"It's time to go Lesley, don't fight it. I told you before, you are such a bad investment, please just die."

I gasped, "Please, just go," I heard his footsteps walking away and was so relieved.

I must have fallen into a deep sleep, I don't know for how long when suddenly I heard the door open and footsteps approaching my bed. I felt someone hold my hand. I opened my eyes hoping it wasn't Bassam. I was so relieved to see the auxiliary nurse who had helped me to the room.

"Hello, Mrs Sehli, how are you feeling?"

"Still poorly," I replied, "Do they know what is wrong with me yet?"

"I am sure they will know soon. You just rest. May I bring you another blanket?"

"Oh yes, thank you."

Tenderly she put the blanket over me, tucking in all the little edges, making me feel so snug and safe.

"What is your name?" I asked her.

"My name is Violet," she smiled.

"You have a beautiful name, Violet. I promise that I will never forget you and the kindness you have shown me this day."

For the next three days, I would be fighting for my life; no one knew yet why I was so ill.

"We have taken a sample from your Hickman Line Lesley, it is now growing in the laboratory," said one of the consultants.

Gosh, I thought, it sounds like I have a triffid or an alien growing inside of me,

"Please get it out" I whispered under my breath.

On the fourth day, thank goodness, they found the culprit. There was a bug in my Hickman Line. This afternoon I will go through a procedure to remove the line and hopefully I will get my body back.

So what was all the fuss about you might ask? Well it wasn't easy but I have just won another very important battle. Against who you might then ask? A very strong contender known as `Septicaemia`.

I have two choices, I can stay wrapped up in this blanket and get on with dying

or,

stand up and fight and get on with living

(Lesley A Sehli 1958 –   )

I have been resting at home and have delayed meeting up with my oncology nurse, Jean. However, on the phone I have mentioned to her that I have some money worries at the moment.

"Don't worry Lesley, there is a woman, called Carol, who works at Maggie's. I will call her and make an appointment for you to see her."

Jean kindly has made the appointment for me with Carol who deals with financial affairs for cancer sufferers.

On the day of my appointment Bassam asked, "Where are you going?".

"I have an appointment at Maggie's with a woman called Carol."

"Why?" he asked.

"Just to go over some things."

"What things?" he said, hanging on to every word I was saying, like a dog with a bone.

"I just want to run something by her, so I would rather be on my own."

"Right, I will take you," he insisted.

As we drove to Maggie's you could have cut the air with a knife.

"I will come in with you. I would like to see this place."

My heart sank, "Bassam please, I need some space. I want to talk to Carol about the fact that I am not working. Seemingly I can have a little allowance to help me through this time, so really you don't have to be there."

"Of course I should be there," he said.

He is just like a sniffer dog whenever money might be involved.

"Hello Carol, it is so lovely to meet you."

"You too, Mrs Sehli, please come through to my room and we can have chat."

"Thank you," I said trying to keep a smile on my face, "This is my husband, Bassam."

"Hello Bassam, nice to meet you, please come through."

As we followed Carol I wanted to scream. She has no idea that I am married to a devil and a thief. She kindly offered us coffee and cake, being ever so kind and welcoming.

"Lesley," she said, "you are going through a lot and I know it will be sometime before you will be able to work again, so I am applying for a financial grant on your behalf."

Although she was so tender and discreet my eyes filled. I was so embarrassed, I had never before in my life asked anyone for money. This shouldn't be, here was I married into a very wealthy and influential family, but living with a high-roller gambler and leach who was making my life hell.

"Please don't be sad Lesley," she said. "This is for you, to help you along the way and give you some peace of mind."

"Thank you," I replied, fully aware that Bassam would try and get a piece of this pie.

She asked me some questions for the paperwork, unknown to her, the final question would seal my doom.

"What is your bank account number, Lesley?"

Bassam immediately interrupted

"Lesley we will put it in our joint account, so the days that that you are feeling poorly I can get it for you."

I smiled to Carol, I wanted to shout out loud 'NO' but I just didn't have the strength anymore. We travelled home together, him with a smirk and I with a heavy heart.

A few weeks later and I have now started my month of radiotherapy. I am still very frail and can't walk very well but this part of the treatment is easy. No pain, no needles, I am just feeling a wee bit tired. This afternoon I have decided to take a wee walk to the bank and see if the cancer fund money has reached the account. If it has I will be able to clear my credit cards and have some peace of mind.

"Hello," I said to the bank teller, "can you check my account please?"

"Are you all right?" she asks me, seeing that I was struggling to walk and catch my breath.

"Oh yes, thank you, I am okay, it's just at this moment in time I am going through cancer treatment and I just get so very tired."

"Oh, I am sorry Mrs Sehli, would you like a seat?"

"No, that's very kind of you. Could you just check my account; I am expecting money from a cancer fund?"

"Oh yes, Mrs Sehli, it arrived to your account three days ago, a total of £1,800."

"Oh great," I said.

"Yes," she replied, "but there is only £200 left."

"How can that be?" I asked her.

"I think you should check with your husband. He debited the money yesterday, a total of £1,600."

I withdrew what was left of the money. I stopped at one of the shoe shops and bought myself a beautiful pair of soft UGG boots, a wee bit of luxury for my tired swollen feet. I then went home, had a good cry, curled up under the blankets to try and sleep and forget this terrible nightmare I was living through. Perhaps I can have peace of mind for a few hours ...

Late afternoon, Bassam returned to the house.

"Bassam," I asked, trying to be polite as possible, knowing that when I asked about my cancer grant money he might flare up yet again.

"This morning, I went to the bank to get some money to clear my visa cards, but the teller said that yesterday you debited £1,800 pounds."

"Yes that's right, I need the money to clear some bills."

"Could you please give it to me, as I need to settle my credit cards."

"Why have you been using your cards?" he asked.

"Because I need to eat, Bassam, and buy necessities for the house. Please just give me the money and I will try to help you with your debts."

"What do you mean bitch, you will try to help me?"

"I called Gam Anon, Bassam. They will help us through your addiction."

"You bitch, shut your mouth, you are getting nothing and I am seeing no-one."

"Please, Bassam, I need the money."

"Well that's not going to happen."

"Please," I screamed, "I don't want to be in debt because of you."

Again, I realised I had gone to far. His eyes became cold, he grabbed me again by the back of my neck and threw me out of the flat. "Get out of here, you sharmouta."

"Stop," I shouted, "this is my home, as I held on to the door handle for dear life."

As he punched my face, I let the door handle go. He grabbed me again and pushed me to the top of the stairs. "I told you to die, you bitch."

"No Bassam, I am not a bitch and I will not die," I screamed.

I lost my footing as he pushed me again at the top of the stairs and …

Everything was a blur., I just continued to fall, then suddenly I stopped at the bottom of the stairwell. I didn't move, I lay quiet. I could hear his footsteps getting nearer. I sensed him standing over me.

"Let me help you," he said.

"Leave me alone," I said, "or I will scream until the neighbours hear me."

Time passed, I waited until I heard his footsteps leave the building, then slowly I climbed back up the stairwell. I felt sore all over, but I knew I had been lucky because of the carpeting on the stairwell.

I called Jenny, but I was so composed.

"Bassam has just punched me and pushed me down the building stairwell."

"Lesley! Are you hurt?"

"I feel a wee bit shaken, to say the least, and a wee bit sore all over. He took my cancer fund money Jenny."

"Oh, Lesley, please call the police."

"I can't Jenny. I am too weak to go through much more of this."

"Lesley, just call them, just to tell them that you are okay you that you just want to register the call, so at least they are aware. Where is he now?"

"I don't know, he left."

"Please Lesley, you have a safe full of guns, it is not safe for you anymore, please call the police and then call me back."

"Okay, Jenny."

As I hung up the phone with Jenny I knew what she was saying was right. I just wished it was all a bad dream from which I would wake up, but of course, it wasn't. I was so worried about involving the police. I just needed someone to talk to him, someone who could show him that what he is doing is wrong, because he really is out of control. Unfortunately, his brother who I have tried to talk to, when he came to Scotland for a visit with his wife, said:

"Marriage is like a see-saw Lesley, it will work out okay if you let Bassam take the lead, and always be on the higher side."

Well that didn't help, it's by giving up my independence, believing and trusting in him as a decent human being that I am in this mess. As for his, so called, friends, well you know the saying 'birds of a feather' ... , all are shady characters, like him. Yes, Jenny's right, I am going to call the police.

"Hello, am I through to Stewarton Police station?"

"Yes, hello, how can I help you?"

"My name is Mrs Sehli, from West George Street, in Glasgow. My husband has just assaulted me."

"The policewoman asked "Are you injured, Mrs Sehli?"

"I am okay. He punched me and pushed me down the stairs. I am a little bit sore but I think I am okay."

"Is he there at the moment?"

"No he left the house, I don't know where he is."

"Okay, stay where you are and we will send some officers over."

"Oh no, I am okay, I just wanted you to record my call in case he does it again."

"Mrs Sehli, are you sure you are okay?"

"Yes, it's just I worry because of the guns in the house and I am not so strong because I am fighting cancer at the moment."

"Would you please come to the police station tomorrow at anytime and just let us know that you are okay?"

"Yes," I said, "I promise."

As I hung up the phone, I felt safe knowing that the police were aware and at least I had evidence if he assaulted me again. Just then the door opened, it was Bassam. Without looking at me he went straight to the master bedroom. Five minutes later the door buzzer went. I viewed the camera and I couldn't believe it, two uniformed policemen were standing at the door. I pressed the entry button and before I knew it they were outside the penthouse door.

"Mrs Sehli, are you okay?"

"Yes," I said quietly.

"Where is your husband?"

"He just got back and has gone through to the master bedroom."

"Please, Mrs Sehli, we need to talk to you and know that you will be alright. We have a car waiting downstairs, would you kindly come back with us to the police station and you can give us a statement?"

"Do I have to? I am sure everything will be alright now."

"Mrs Sehli, it is just so we can sit with you a little while and know that you are safe. We will park the car round the corner and wait for you there, so none of your neighbours will notice."

"Okay, I will see you there, I will just get my coat."

As I quietly left the apartment, unbeknown to Bassam, I took the private elevator. I was starting to feel quite drained and bruises were appearing on my arms and the side of my face from the fall. As we arrived at the police station it all seemed so very surreal. At the station they were so very kind. They took me to a small interview room were I told them what had happened.

About one hour later they asked if I would now sign the statement which would give them the go ahead to bring Bassam into custody. I realise now, in hindsight, that I should have signed but at that moment in time, I just didn't want any more hassle. Instead I asked that they just talk to him.

"Mrs Sehli we are going now to bring him to the station for questioning. However, if he admits that he has assaulted you then we will be arresting him."

They thoughtfully gave me a cup of coffee as I sat in the waiting room. About twenty minutes later, I saw through the glazed window the burly outline of Bassam, with the officers, being escorted to another room. About an hour later Bassam came out with the officers to the waiting room where I was sitting. He was now free to go.

He hadn't admitted guilt and I hadn't signed the statement, but at least I thought he will have learned a very big lesson; no more abuse as the police are now aware of his antics. As we went to get a taxi back home, I thought he would apologise, but with his ice cold stare he said:

"What have you done? I might lose my gun license because of you."

I should have known!

Another month has passed and now I am going to start the last treatment phase of the miracle cancer drug Herseptin, which I will receive intravenously on a three-week cycle, for one year. I am feeling a little stronger. I now have tiny baby curls which are starting to appear, although at the moment, I am still using my wee pink scarf. My walking is still a problem but I am sure that given time I will get the powerful Lesley back. In case you are wondering about Bassam, I hardly ever see him. I hear him returning in the middle of the night from his activities. This marriage, as you will have already surmised, is doomed. As soon as I complete this treatment, I hope somehow to start my business, obtain an agreeable divorce settlement and be as far away from him as possible.

Aunt Helen has joined me today, as this will be my first Herseptin treatment which will hopefully allow me to live. I am not too sure what to expect. Cathy has told me it is a small needle, unlike the one that was used during my chemotherapy, so I am feeling okay and relaxed about this other wee adventure. To help me through, I hear in my mind the words of Sarah, which will be permanently imprinted on to my heart.

"You are such a lucky girl Lesley. You are a match to receive the miracle drug. You have a good chance to survive, stay strong."

As Cathy hooked me up and the drip started, Aunt Helen smiled, "You are doing well, Lesley."

For a couple of minutes I felt cold and a little dizzy, but those feelings soon passed. At the other end of the room was an older lady who looked so pale and very ill.

"Gosh," I said to Aunt Helen, "poor thing I hope she will be okay."

As the day went on I was feeling so relaxed. Pat, the volunteer, arrived to spoil us with tempting sandwiches and cakes. A few more hours passed and the older lady, who I thought was at death's door, had finished her drip and was walking towards Aunt Helen and I.

My, how different she looked. Her paleness had disappeared and been replaced by beautiful rosy cheeks. That must be some miracle drug that she is on. I hope that is what they are giving me.

"What's a young lassie like you doing in here?" she asked me, with a true Glasgow accent.

"Oh," I smiled, "I am a cancer patient and today I have just started this miracle drug, Herseptin. What's your name?" I asked.

"My name is Ina" she replied.

"Hello, Ina, I am so pleased to meet you. This is my Aunt Helen."

"Hello, Helen," she smiled.

"Did you have chemotherapy?" she asked.

"Oh yes, Ina, I did."

"Me too hen, but I couldn't finish it, because I was just too sick, but like you I'm a match for this miracle drug."

"I was just saying to Aunt Helen what beautiful rosy cheeks you have."

"Och, thank you, hen, nae bad for a woman in her late seventies."

"That's for sure Ina. Which part of Glasgow are you from?"

"The East End hen."

"Me too, Ina."

"Och Aye hen, I can tell you are a friendly wee soul. There is nothing like the Glasgow banter, isn't that right, Helen?"

"Absolutely, Ina."

"So Ina," I asked, "how did you get here? Who is with you?"

"Nobody is with me hen. I came all the way on a bus. I haven't got anybody hen."

Oh dear, I thought, how sad, this precious old lady going through all this on her own. Thank goodness that the nursing team around her are so wonderful and kind. I know they will make her feel very special and that she is not alone.

"Well hen, I'm going hame noo. It was lovely tae meet you."

"Me too, Ina. I tell you what, at our next Herseptin clinic would you like to join me for coffee at the wee reception coffee shop?"

Her face lit up. "I would love that, hen."

"Okay," I smiled "it's a date."

Aunt Helen watched her as Ina went off with a big smile on her face.

"I think she knows, Lesley, that she has just met a new friend."

Five minutes later a smart woman in a tailored suit walked through the door.

"Hello Helen, Hello Lesley."

My face lit up, with the biggest smile, my best friend; my beautiful mum had arrived.

"Mum what are you doing here?" I asked (although I was delighted, I had never wanted her to see me in this state, with needles and monitors).

"Och, hen, I am just too nosey. I wanted to see my wee lassie and get all the gossip from your Aunt Helen."

How we laughed. Pat brought everyone more coffee and we chatted the whole afternoon. Eight hours later my drip was removed and I felt on top of the world!

Three weeks later, I met Ina as I had promised and treated her to some coffee and cake at the hospital coffee shop an hour before our treatment would start.

"How are you feeling Ina?"

"Och, I am okay hen, it's just I have a lot of pain under this arm."

"Oh don't worry Ina," I replied, "it's the same for me. It is because the cancer had gone in to our lymph nodes and they had to remove some of them, but given time the pain will go."

"Och, no hen," she said, "it's because of the supermarket trolley."

"What do you mean Ina?"

"Och hen," she said, "I live on the third floor of a tenement building and its pulling the supermarket trolley up the close and then up three flights of stairs that has done my wee arm in," she said, with the biggest chuckle.

"My goodness, Ina," I said, "what an inspiration you are!"

Six months have passed and I only have another six months left to complete my 'miracle drug' treatment. I am feeling stronger, however, my walking seems to be a bit of an issue. Guess what?! My eyebrows and eyelashes are back and at last. I have been able to say goodbye, and thank you, to my wee pink scarf. I am starting to admire, once again, my reflection in the mirror. One might call this vanity, but I do appreciate my head of golden curls.

I have been to a lawyer regarding separation from Bassam, but as I have little money, he really wasn't interested and his manner was of a well-dressed chauvinistic person. I need to find a lawyer who will agree to take me on and help me. Someone who has principles, a human rights type of person.

I have emailed and called my brother-in-law, Talal, regarding my situation and he just keeps saying, "Talk to Bassam," – What a great help that is – I don't think!

"I need somewhere to live, Talal."

"Okay Lesley, have a look at some houses and then email me the information."

Emile has been calling me from America.

"Oh Lesley your situation is terrible, you are going through so much, I shouldn't have introduced you to Bassam. He is so bad."

"Emile, it was my decision to date him, but the information you gave me before I dated him was all untrue and for that, I am so disappointed in you."

"Oh Lesley, Talal will help you get a home and if he doesn't you could write a book."

"What do you mean Emile?"

"Well, you have been through so much and here in America they love true stories just like yours. It is terrible what the family are doing to you. If you wrote a book about what you have been through, I am sure it would make a great movie."

"Oh no, surely it would never come to that," I said.

These words from Emile would have a lasting impact on me. The seed was planted and unbeknown to me at this time, its shoots would eventually grow.

It's the weekend and I am off to visit mum and dad. I am going to cook them a delectable meal, so I have got my wee bag of spices and of course a bottle of fine wine. I hailed a taxi from the shopping centre and while putting on my seat belt, the driver started to move. Suddenly, the taxi was being shoved sideways, as though by a giant snow plough. I screamed! Eventually, we stopped and everything went quiet and black for a minute or so. What has happened? I knew I was bleeding as droplets of blood were dripping on to my blouse. I think it's my head. The door that I was sitting beside opened and a lady reached for my hand.

"It's okay dear, you will be okay, your taxi has crashed and an ambulance is on the way."

I had been sitting on the right side behind the driver, who thankfully I could see was also alive and was now beside the woman who was talking to me. When I turned to my left I couldn't believe what I was seeing. The passenger side, car door was gone and where the door should have been was the front of double decker bus, wedged inches from me. As I looked up the shocked bus driver was just staring at me, looking so bewildered as I looked back at him, mirroring his expression

"Hello there," said a friendly voice, "I am one of the paramedics. What is your name?"

"My name is Lesley," I said.

"Okay, Lesley, we are going to get you into the ambulance."

"Oh, I think I am bleeding," I told her.

"Don't worry, we will help you as soon as we get you out of the taxi and check you properly. Can you move your legs for me?"

"Yes," I said, as she gently helped me out of the car with her colleague, and into the waiting ambulance. A small crowd had gathered, but thankfully I could see no one else was hurt. I was made comfortable in the back of the ambulance as the lovely paramedic started to remove tiny pieces of broken glass from my hair and face.

"Oh you are a lucky girl" she said, "the bleeding is from splintered glass and you will just have some scratches and bruising. Are you feeling sore, Lesley?"

"Yes, my neck a little."

"Okay, we will be at the hospital soon and you will be thoroughly checked there. Please try and relax, I have a few more pieces of glass to remove from all these little curls on your head."

"Oh," I said "last month it would have been easier for you."

"How's that?" she remarked.

"Well, last month I had no hair."

"Oh," she said, "have you been unwell?"

"Yes sort of, I am fighting cancer."

"Oh my, you are going through the wars."

Oh yes, you could say that, it must be all that lucky white heather!

At the hospital I was given a thorough check up. Thank goodness my wounds were superficial and I just needed to wear a neck brace for a couple of days.

"The police are waiting outside Mrs Sehli. They will have a wee word with you."

"Okay," I said, "I just have to call my parents."

"Hello mum, sorry I'm bit late, I have been a bit delayed."

"Is everything okay, Lesley?"

"Oh yes, mum, could you ask dad to pick me up at the Royal Infirmary?"

"Gosh, Lesley, what's wrong?"

"Oh, nothing mum, everything is okay, my taxi crashed but I am absolutely fine."

Two friendly police constables asked me a few questions concerning anything I could remember.

"You know, Mrs Sehli, you are a very lucky lady. You had a narrow escape."

"Really?" I said.

"Yes, you survived because you were sitting behind the driver on the right side of the car which stayed intact, unlike the left side. The bus driver has claimed responsibility. It appears as though it was a freak accident," he continued, as he handed me my shopping bag with, can you believe it, my bottle of wine still intact!

Two days later I was back at hospital for my Herseptin day. As I walked into the room to sit at my chair, with bruises and neck brace, I could feel all eyes on me and sensed the other women were worried. One of the ladies across the room shouted,

"Hey Blondie, what happened to you?"

"Well Jeannie," I whispered, as she and the other ladies leaned forward in their chairs, anxiously waiting for my reply as to what happened to me.

"You know that expression one says when feeling poorly or a wee bit down?" I said.

"What's that?" asked Jeannie.

"I feel like I have been hit by a double decker bus."

"Yes, and so?" she said, hanging on to my every word.

"Well," I laughed, "guess what? I really was! Two days ago I was hit by a double decker bus."

The other women weren't sure whether to laugh or cry. You could have heard a pin drop till Jeannie shouted out "Lucky White Heather, Lesley."

"Yes" I smiled, looking around me, as all the brave ladies attached to drips erupted into laugher.

June 2010

How time flies. I only have three months to complete my Herseptin treatment at the hospital. I have been told that if I survive for the next 10 years, I will be cured. So here's hoping I will reach 2018 and Monsieur Cancer will never visit me again. My walking is still a bit of a problem and I still suffer from fatigue but hopefully when the Herseptin treatment is finally over my body will start to mend itself.

I have talked with Talal on the phone and have told him about my idea of starting a new business. He seems convinced by my idea and said he will help me in getting set up. I have my eyes on a beautiful white house on the Island of Arran. The views from each window are breathtaking, overlooking an endless sandy beach and an ocean as far as the eye can see, its tepid waters kept calm by the ebb and flow of the Gulf stream. A little part of paradise in Scotland, which I know would be a perfect sanctuary for women needing respite after their cancer treatment. My dream would be that Saudi women be given the chance to come over and be rejuvenated on this beautiful island. I have costed the business so as well as helping others, it would give me a chance to be independent and give something back to humanity. I am waiting for Talal's reply, so here's hoping.

With regards to Bassam, well, no changes there. We still live together but I keep out his way as much as I can. He went recently on an expedition to Jordan with a lovely older gentleman called John, a scientist whom he befriended. They went on a trade mission 'Rebuilding Iraq'. Since he came back he hasn't talked about the venture nor have I seen him with the scientist again. I hope he hasn't been up to any of his tricks, as I know since the day I married him, he can never be trusted. Talal did say that if I was to be successful in any business venture, I must make sure that Bassam was never involved, which believe you me, I am now more than aware of. In fact, once he returns all my money from my indemnity which he has borrowed and I have my home, he can take the 'High Road'. His manipulation of me will soon be over! I am still waiting for Talal to get back to me. I have emailed him but nothing as yet.

My father has just informed me that he had loaned Bassam £12,000, for three months, two years ago, the same month I was diagnosed with cancer. I am shocked and saddened as Mum and I had known nothing about it. Two days later Mum and I sat down with Bassam,

"Bassam," I said "how could you take money from my father?"

"I will return it next week," he said.

"You must, Bassam," said mum, "it must go back to my husband's account immediately."

I looked at him, how could I have brought this thief into my family? It's like the Trojan Horse of Troy; he is destroying everyone around me. One week later and still Bassam had not deposited the money back to my father's account. I called Talal telling him what had transpired and that Bassam had still not returned the money.

Talal said, "Talk to him again, Lesley".

Mum said, "Give me the phone, Lesley. Talal I need the money to be returned to my husband's account as soon as possible."

"Oh May," he said to mum, "give him time. I am sure he will return the money."

"Don't whitewash this Talal, (I was so proud of her as I listened) I need that money to be in my husband's account by tomorrow."

Next day, Talal sent the money directly to my parents account, he certainly didn't want a duel with my mum.

A few months later I would find out through many documents and letters that so many people had been hurt by Bassam, both men and women, young and old, some even about to lose the roofs over their heads because of his antics.

September has arrived and I have finished my cancer therapy. Whoopee!!!

I am going to meet up with my wonderful oncology nurse, Jean, for a wee chat and to discuss the issues I have with my walking. I still can't get off the floor unless I hold onto something or someone helps me. It will of course most likely be teething problems after the various treatments I have been going through. Bassam is away, saying he was going to London for a three-day business trip, but what he says doesn't matter anymore. In one ear and out the other.

I arrived at the hospital to meet Jean.

"Good morning, Jean".

"Good morning Lesley, how are you?"

"I am fine, thank you Jean, but I am having terrible problems with Bassam. Unfortunately, my husband is a high roller gambler, womaniser, and abuser."

"I am so sorry to hear this Lesley, goodness you have had a lot to deal with, haven't you?"

"Oh yes Jean, I am just biding time until I get my strength back. There is nothing about him that I wish to salvage in this marriage, except my rights. As we speak, he told me that he was off to London for a three-day business trip, but I found out he is seeing a woman called Amanda there; one of his many conquests."

"How do you know this, Lesley?"

"He left one of his mobiles by mistake at home and I heard it ring. I looked at the miscalls and the name Amanda popped up. I immediately called her back but it went on to voicemail, so I left her a message asking if she could kindly return my call. About five minutes later she called me back and asked me who I was. I told her that my name is Lesley, and I believed we had a mutual friend. She told me that the number I was calling from was her boyfriend, Stephen's number, whose nickname was Dodi. I then asked her if he was Arabic, to which she replied "Yes, from Saudi Arabia."

"Oh Jean, it was terrible. He is so vile and dishonest."

"Did you tell her who you were, Lesley?"

"Yes, I told her he was my husband and his name was Bassam. At this, she accused me of lying as he had told her he was divorced."

She then said, "Oh well, you can't be much of a wife if he is seeing other women."

I then told her, "I am fighting cancer, Amanda, but one thing I will tell you is that you are one of many."

She then told me she was sorry that I had cancer, but my husband was very good to her and her son, taking her to casinos and buying her lots of nice things.

She now knows the truth about him, and hopefully soon, if it's in my power, all the other women that he has betrayed will realise what he is, before he destroys them.

"Lesley, how brave you are," said Jean.

"Thank you, Jean, really it's all about survival at the moment, but one day I will have justice. I am so tired of living like a pauper, waiting for whenever he thinks that it is the right time to throw me a crust of bread. I have spoken to my brother-in-law, Talal, about a house and setting up a business to help people who have been going through cancer, but as yet I am still waiting for his answer. Jean you have been so kind to me through all this ordeal in my life. I promise you as I get stronger, I will turn my life around and I will never forget your kindness."

"Lesley, what about your walking?"

"Still not very good."

"Have you ever thought about getting a small dog. It would be lovely company for you while you recuperate and by walking you will exercise your muscles and in time get stronger? I myself have two little Shih Tzus. They are easy to manage and have lovely temperaments."

"Oh Jean, what a good idea. I think I might just do that."

As I left the hospital my mobile rang, it was Bassam "My trip to London has been delayed till tomorrow, so as I am passing by the hospital, I can pick you up," As I got into his latest toy, a brand new Lexus, he asked me,

"How was your meeting with Jean?"

"Fine, thank you, in fact she has suggested I get a little dog to help me walk and get stronger."

"Really?" he said.

"Yes, really, in fact when I get home I am going to Google small breeds,"

"I tell you what Lesley, I will buy you a dog but I need a favour," he said staring at my diamond-encrusted Rolex watch, on my arm. This is my only prized possessions left from the time he removed everything else from my jewellery box which he deemed valuable, selling or pawning for his addiction while I was so very ill.

"What do you want this time Bassam?"

"I need to borrow your watch Lesley, the one on your arm."

I looked straight at him and said with a smile, knowing too well I would not see my watch again.

"Sure, Bassam, stop the car for a moment."

He drew into a parking lane, while I proceeded to bring a paper and pen from my bag.

"What are you doing," he said.

"I am writing this paper which I need you to sign, showing all my jewellery including this watch which you are going to borrow and have promised to give me back. You have also to pay off all my credit cards which are at the maximum because of your gambling and that you have promised to clear."

I knew at that point he was desperate, I smiled as he signed the paper, knowing full well that I would never see my watch again. I would get a dog and have his written confession. Yes, at last I am standing up to him, and this is only the beginning!

The following week I went with him to choose a puppy from the mining village of Dalmellington. The Shih Tzu puppies were on sale for £400.

"Hello," said a welcoming lady, "my name is Catherine. Are you Mrs Sehli?"

"Yes Catherine, I am, but you can call me Lesley and this is my husband, Bassam."

Catherine showed us through to a room with a big playpen holding a number of tiny six week old Shih Tzu puppies.

"Oh Catherine, they are all so beautiful."

"Would you like to go inside the pen Lesley, and sit with them?"

"Oh, I would love to Catherine, but I am not so strong on my legs at the moment."

"Oh, don't worry" she said kindly, "I will help you."

Catherine gently helped me into the pen, to sit down amongst all these wonderful furry babies.

"Take your time Lesley, they all have very different personalities."

"Are they male or female Catherine?"

"There is one female, Lesley, but she has already been sold. The others are all boys."

I looked around, how does one choose? They were all so delightful. As I turned to the side, in the far corner I saw one of them just sitting, staring at me. Although still small he was the biggest of the litter, just like a little Buddha. I pointed him out to Catherine.

"Oh," she said with a smile, "that's the first born, the friendly bully."

"What do you mean, friendly bully, Catherine?"

"Oh well, he eats first, finishes last, then goes and snoozes on top of his little brothers and sister."

"May I hold him Catherine?"

"Of course, Lesley" she said, handing me this tiny furry baby that fitted into the palm of my hand.

He looked up at me, gave a lick to the side of my cheek and then fell fast asleep.

"Oh Catherine, I think I have found my boy".

"Well Lesley, he is yours, but I can't give him to you until he is eight weeks old."

I looked to Bassam from the floor of the pen, "This little puppy is my choice, Bassam."

"Okay," he said looking at Catherine. "How much?" he asked her bluntly.

"As advertised, Mr Bassam, £400, but if you like you can leave just a deposit until you come back and collect him in two weeks' time."

"I will pay you £300 for the puppy," he said.

"I am sorry, as advertised the puppies are £400."

He brought out a wad of £100 notes. "If you make it £300, I will give it to you right now, instead of a deposit."

"No, I am sorry, Mr Bassam, as I already said, the puppies were advertised at £400."

He looked at me nervously, "Well Lesley let's go and we can think about it," he said, as he rudely walked to the door.

"No Bassam, I am not going to think about it. I want this puppy."

I looked to Catherine, "I am so sorry Catherine," I whispered in a low voice so as Bassam wouldn't hear me. "Please say yes to the £300 which he has offered you and when I come to pick the puppy up I will give you the other £100."

"Okay Lesley, don't worry I will keep him for you and if you like I will bring him to you at your home."

"Oh, thank you so very much Catherine," I replied, as she helped me stand up and climb out of the pen I handed her back the puppy.

"What do you think?" I asked her, "I would like to call him Hamish."

She smiled "I will bring Hamish home to you, Lesley, in two weeks' time."

As soon as I got in the car, Bassam sped off.

"You see, another deal done and it was only £300."

I smiled and thought, if you only knew!

Two weeks later Catherine arrived at my home with wee Hamish. I placed him in his cosy sheepskin bed, surrounded by toys. Catherine and I chatted a while over a cup of tea as I handed her a pretty velvet box of chocolates with the £100 placed neatly under the first layer. As Catherine left I picked up my little boy, Hamish. As he snuggled in my arms I felt so very happy and content. What a beautiful moment of Unconditional Love.

The Greatest Loss of All

I so enjoy this time, there is a lot of snow, so it looks like it is going to be a white Christmas. I called mum this morning, but there is no answer, she is probably out with dad Christmas shopping. One hour later my phone rings.

"Lesley, it's dad".

"Hi dad, I've been trying to call you."

"Lesley, I am at the hospital with mum."

"Why dad?"

"In the middle of the night your mum was feeling sick, we are here at the emergency department."

"Okay dad, I will be with you in about twenty minutes."

The snow was really heavy as the taxi arrived.

"Royal Infirmary please, as quick as you can."

As we drove through the streets visibility was becoming very poor, roads were being blocked off because of the amount of snow that was falling. The traffic was coming to a standstill, with traffic jams everywhere.

"Oh," I said to the driver, "this is terrible. Maybe I should try and walk, my mum has just been taken into hospital."

"Don't you worry hen," he said in a broad Glasgow twang, "I have been driving taxis for twenty-five years, I know every nook and cranny. I will get you there in five minutes. There is a wee short cut at the end this road."

Sure enough, five minutes later we were arriving at the hospital, as a weather warning came from the radio announcing that Glasgow and surrounding areas would have a very heavy snowfall. People were being advised to limit their travel and buses and taxis would be off the road until further notice.

"Thank you so much," I said to the driver, giving him a wee tip as I battled the blizzard.

"Stay indoors lassie," he said, "till this storm dies doon."

"Oh yes," I shouted, making my way in to the casualty department. There were lots of cubicles with people being attended to by doctors and nurses as I nervously scanned the room looking for mum. Dad saw me and approached.

"Where is mum? Dad what's happening?"

"She is in that cubicle, Lesley" he said, pointing to the left.

I looked over and saw mum smiling at me, but she was so pale. As I walked closer to her with dad, my heart was about to stop when dad said,

"Your mum has cancer, Lesley."

For the next week my mum would try to win her fight. Dad and Aunt Helen and I waited by her side as other members of the family arrived. They operated, she was doing so well. Unbeknown to my father or anybody else I walked every day to the hospital and back as all the roads where I lived were blocked off. It took me an hour to get there and another hour to return home. I stayed all day at the hospital waiting for mum to get better. On the fifth day her condition started to deteriorate.

"What's wrong with me, Lesley?"

"Mum, you will be okay, just like me. I need you to fight mum, please keep strong. I love you."

"Lesley, I need you to make sure your father gets his shopping at Morrison's and tell your Auntie Anne I love her very much," (Auntie Anne was mum's wee sister, who had special needs).

"Mum, please, you will be fine. I need you. Who will I talk to?"

"Your Aunt Helen," she smiled, "talk to your Aunt Helen … Lesley can you put water on my lips?"

"Of course mum, and can I brush your hair?"

"Yes Lesley, that will be nice."

That same evening mum was moved to a quiet room, surrounded by her family. I held her hand, the monitor stopped as she took one last breath.

My pain was intense; unlike anything I have ever known. My world would be changed forever!!

Million Dollar Deal

April 2011

Four months have gone by and apart from fatigue, I am physically much stronger. Talal finally agreed to my business plan and I am travelling tomorrow, for ten days, to the family home in Saudi Arabia. Bassam is still refusing to join me, even though Talal has insisted that he travel with me.

"Remember Lesley," said Talal, "this business project which I am offering to help you with, is with the stipulation that Bassam has no involvement. I don't want him anywhere near it."

"Don't worry, Talal, I will personally take care of all aspects of the running of the business. I will keep you in the loop at all times and I can assure you that Bassam will have no involvement whatsoever."

I am travelling with an old friend of Talal's. She is a British hotelier called Judy and her brother Simon is travelling with her. He is an economist with whom I have shared my ideas regarding a Cancer Wellbeing Centre for Saudi women. I am not sure, unlike Talal, that involving Judy in this venture is the right thing to do. I think she is a lot older than me, of course that is neither here nor there, but she appears very opinionated and rather bossy. She is materialistic and devoid of empathy, not someone I would normally socialise with or share a business venture with. It is only because of Talal's persistence that I invited her on this business trip with me. (He knew her years ago when she was working in Saudi Arabia, allegedly, as a personal trainer.)

At last the three of us are on a flight to the beautiful city of Acabar in Jordan, where we will stay for one night. I feel so happy, that at last I have a chance to build myself a life again. When all the ground work is completed hopefully I can convince Bassam, to return to Saudi Arabia and be with his family, while I turn my business plan into, hopefully, a very profitable venture, while at the same time helping women from a country that I have loved so much.

Talal was kind enough to book us into a luxury hotel and my bedroom has a balcony overlooking the hotel's pool, and a panoramic view of the sea. This is so the life I had before I married Bassam, and how I miss it.

The next day, Talal's driver arrived at the hotel to drive us across the border and into Saudi Arabia. The heat was intense, as we covered a great distance of desert and dunes, passing many Bedouin encampments along the way. I was feeling exhilarated; at last, back in my Arabia.

Early evening, we arrived at one of the family mansions. We were met at the door by Talal and my sister-in-law Faisa. I felt welcomed by Faisa but received a cold reception from Talal. Why, I wondered, I hope he hasn't changed his mind? The driver took Judy and Simon off to a hotel while I was shown to my quarters in the mansion. That night we had dinner in one of the many dining rooms of the house. It was pleasant enough but the atmosphere was heavy.

"Why did Bassam not come with you Lesley?" asked Talal.

"He just refused. He is totally out of control, that's why I asked you for your help to build this project of the wellbeing centre."

"Yes, I understand that," he said abruptly, "but you should have got Bassam here."

He seemed to look right through me, my heart began to sink. I think I have been hoodwinked. Talal doesn't want to help me, he just wants his brother back.

That night, I lay in bed, tossing and turning, feeling so very alone, and how I missed my beautiful mum. My body was hurting, as I am still not as strong as I used to be and my walking is still not great. What if Talal doesn't help me. What will I do? What will become of me?

Next morning, the maid had prepared breakfast for Faisa, her two children and I, beside the pool. It was so lovely chatting with Faisa who was now happily expecting baby number three.

"Why don't you come back and live here in Saudi Arabia with Bassam, Lesley?"

"Honestly Faisa, I will, if I can get a business going and persuade Bassam to return back. The problem is, as I am sure you know, Bassam is a high roller gambler and unfortunately he has been destroying everything in his path, including me. It's been a tough time Faisa, especially having lost mum. She was such a wonderful woman and I know she will be proud of what I am trying to achieve. If I get my project off the ground Faisa, I can secure my life again and help so many."

"Inshalla, Lesley. I hope so. Now, Talal has asked that you be ready by 11.00 a.m. He will pick you up to go and see some of the lands belonging to the family."

"Thank you Faiza, for your hospitality and being so kind. I will go now and get ready."

Sure enough, a little after 11.00 a.m., Talal arrives at the front of the house in his four-wheel drive, accompanied by his stepbrother, Hani (my previous boss in Paris).

"Salaam, Lesley," said Hani, who I was so happy to see, although I will never forget the two questions he asked me when we were in the car.

"Does Bassam have a British passport yet Lesley?"

To which I answered, "No, he has residence only."

"Has he been gambling again?"

"Yes, all the time and it is even worse now than it was when I first found out. I have tried everything to help him, including all the advice you gave me, Talal," I said, looking directly at him through the rear-view mirror in the car.

"Does he pray or go to the mosque?" asked Talal.

"Unfortunately, rarely," I answered.

Talal and Hani then continued talking in Arabic. I tried to hear what they were saying, but it was too difficult from where I was seated at the back of the car.

Again, Talal, staring at me through the rear-view mirror said, "You should have brought him with you Lesley."

"With full respect Talal, you can bring a horse to water but you cannot make it drink," I replied.

Hani turned to me and said, "He is bad Lesley. He is not a good man."

I sat quietly, looking at both of them with a heavy heart, asking myself, was coming all this way worth it, but at the same time knowing that I had to stick it out to be able to find a way to turn my life around. Talal gave me a running commentary, pointing out the vast lands and properties they owned. We then gathered at the family farm for a delicious rustic Arabian lunch, meeting up with Judy and Simon who were asking so many questions regarding the business they wanted to set up.

"It would be an elegant spa with a beauty salon and every type of treatment for the wealthy Saudi women to indulge in," said Judy.

I looked at her.

"No! That is not what the business is about Judy. It is a Cancer Wellbeing Centre for daily respite for women, regardless of wealth. The business plan I have put together will be profitable for all, yet giving a lot to society."

Judy looked at me with a condescending manner, "Well, Lesley, my speciality is beauty and I think that is the way to go."

"No," I said, looking at Talal for support, but there wasn't any. Surprise, Surprise!

By this time, I had deduced that Talal and the family had no intention of helping me, they had only wanted their brother back and I had been the decoy, but of course that hadn't worked. So many lies, such deceit from Talal and betrayal from Judy. What's happening in my life? Mum used to tell me that everything I touched turned to gold. I must continue and never give up. I know that soon I will find a way to start spinning gold once again.

That night I made a few calls to friends and colleagues I had known in Jeddah and to a women's wellbeing centre I had heard about that dealt with a variety of women's issues. Perhaps they would be interested in my project? I called and asked if it would be possible in three days' time to have a meeting with the Director, before I travelled back to the London.

"I have a training package that I would like to discuss with your Director."

"Yes, Mrs Sehli, the Directors name is Madame Suzanne and I have made you an appointment to see her at 11.00 a.m. next week, if that is suitable for you?"

"Oh yes, thank you," I replied.

That same night I informed Faisa that I would be leaving the day after tomorrow and that I would like to speak with Talal, privately tomorrow morning, before he goes to his office.

Next morning, after breakfast, I sat quietly in one of the salons of the mansion, while I waited for Talal to appear. Looking out of the window, believe it or not, you looked directly into the swimming pool as though one was peering into an aquarium and I smiled as the children dived down, waving at me through the glass. Ten minutes later Talal appeared, his demeanour as though I was having an audience with the king.

"Good Morning, Talal," I smiled.

"Good Morning," he said, as he invited me to walk with him to another area of the house and take a seat.

"You wanted to talk to me, Lesley. Faisa has said that you wish to leave tomorrow?"

"Yes, Talal, to you and Faisa I say, thank you, for your hospitality, but it is obvious that you have decided not to help me with my venture."

He said nothing.

"Talal, I am not going to beg, but I need help from you, even if it's a loan to get on my feet. I am part of this family and I have been going through hell and still am because of your brother."

"What do you want?" he said abruptly, looking at his watch.

"This is my life I am talking about, Talal, as you are well aware. I need security and to get stability back into my life."

"Yes, I understand that," he answered, curtly. "So, what can I do for you?"

"I need a house to live in, in Scotland, and an allowance like Bassam has from the family until I get on my feet. I will not survive if I stay with Bassam. He is verbally, physically and emotionally abusing me and he needs to be stopped."

"Anything else?" he said, as though I was a beggar from the street.

"No, thank you," I said, with assertiveness, "I only need enough money to buy the house in Arran that I have already discussed with you and an allowance like the rest of the family, until my project commences."

"Okay, I will see what I can do," he said, with his usual abrupt manner.

"Thank you, Talal."

"Faisa has told me you are leaving to Jeddah tomorrow for some business?"

"Yes, a women's wellbeing centre and from there I will return to London."

He then got up to go saying, "The driver will take you to the airport tomorrow to catch your flight."

"Thank you," I said, fearing the worst, knowing in my heart that yet again he would probably let me down. Our talk took all of ten minutes with no empathy, no sincerity. I should have known, to them I am a woman, an infidel, and a foreigner. I was clutching at straws, but, I had no choice, I was still fighting to survive.

I arrived in Jeddah, next morning, and checked into a comfortable hotel. I met up with some friends for lunch and in the evening had dinner with my lovely Luz, (my previous maid in Jeddah) we had so much catching up to do.

"Luz, I am sorry things haven't worked out the way I hoped, but I promise that when I start to turn my life around and get my wellbeing centre going, I will find you and if you still want the position of housekeeper, it will be yours."

"Oh yes, Mam Lesley," she said, "I will look forward to that day."

The next day I arrived at the villa of the women's wellbeing centre, for my appointment with the Director, Suzanne. It was a very welcoming place, cool and decorated with light pastel colours, set amid a lush garden of flowers.

"Please, have a seat," the friendly receptionist said, "the Director will be with you shortly."

As I waited, my hopes were high that the woman I was about to meet would be interested in my project. Perhaps from this villa I would eventually start giving inspirational talks to women going through cancer, to empower them through the rough patch in their lives. I wonder where the Director is from? She has an Arabic surname, perhaps she is Saudi or from one of the other Gulf states. As one of the doors opened an elegant lady with the most gentile smile walked towards me.

"Hello, Mrs Sehli, pleased to meet you. My name is Suzanne."

"Hello, Suzanne, it is lovely to meet you", I said, as I followed her through to her office.

As we entered her room there were pretty flowers in vases, framed family pictures and lots of books. I felt so comfortable in her presence, through both her demeanour and her charm.

"Would you like a refreshing cup of tea Lesley?" she asked.

"Yes thank you, that would be lovely."

"So Lesley, where are you from? My secretary tells me that you have just arrived from the northern region?"

"Yes, I am from Scotland and I am visiting my husband's family, hoping to start a business venture, but I feel that Jeddah has more prospects."

"Well yes, Lesley, Jeddah is much bigger and perhaps more cosmopolitan."

"Yes, I realise that because I worked here for 21 years, before I married."

"Oh my, Lesley," she said, "that is a long time. So, I am sure you know the culture well? Is your husband travelling with you Lesley?"

"No he prefers to relax back in Scotland, but I do hope he will spend some time here soon."

(I hoped, in the future, I would be able to tell Suzanne about my situation, but at this moment the meeting was about business and I didn't want my personal life to interfere.)

I continued to explain to Suzanne my ideas about my business projects, at the same time showing her some catalogues and examples of prosthesis for women undergoing mastectomies: artificial implants, wigs, colourful scarves for wearing at home, gels to cool them at night while undergoing chemotherapy and pretty lingerie and swimwear for the feel good days.

"Oh my, Lesley," she said, "you have worked hard on this venture, even though you have been so sick yourself."

"Thank you, Suzanne."

"Are you going to charge money for these talks?"

"Yes, not too much, just enough to make a living."

(At this point she must have wondered why I was doing this, when I had a husband at home in Scotland who was from a wealthy family. Whatever the case, she was very kind and discreet, saying nothing.)

As we chatted, before long I realised that we shared a lot of goals, specifically pertaining to projects for the wellbeing of women.

"Lesley, this is a small villa but we have rooms which I could rent out to you at a competitive rate. Let me show you around."

It was amazing. The villa was beautiful, so fresh and spacious with rooms well equipped for my presentations and beautiful merchandise. As we returned back to Suzanne's office she asked me how I would market my idea.

"I would use social media, Saudia Airlines, where I still have a lot of contacts, and send flyers to the hospitals," I replied.

"Great," she said, "and when are you returning to London?"

"Day after tomorrow."

"Then can you come back and see me tomorrow, I like your idea Lesley and there is someone I would like you to meet."

I smiled, "Thank you so much Suzanne, that would be lovely."

That evening I felt, yet again, as though I was floating on air. Tomorrow, I hope, will be a great day and the chance to make my dreams come true.

The next morning, I asked the driver on the way to the villa to kindly stop at the patisserie so as to pick up some pastries for my meeting with Suzanne.

"Good Morning," said Suzanne, as I entered her office. "This is my friend Barbara who also lives here in Saudi Arabia."

"Hi Lesley," she said, with her American accent, giving a broad smile, "nice to meet you."

What a lovely afternoon we had, as we chatted about my project and business plan over a pot of tea and the delicious pastries.

"I am a cancer patient also Lesley, and I am now terminal." said Barbara.

For a moment my thoughts went back to Sarah in the hospital whom I had met at my first chemotherapy.

"Well, Barbara, you look brand new," I told her, "I would never have known."

"Thanks Lesley, I am doing well and I am very interested in your project. As Suzanne will verify, I know a lot of women who could help you, on a volunteer basis, to get your project off the ground."

My heart was racing; this was music to my ears, manna from heaven.

"I was thinking," said Suzanne, "what about a hospice, Lesley?"

"Sorry?" I said, not exactly sure what she was meaning.

"Yes, Lesley, we could build a hospice. It would be the first ever in Saudi Arabia."

I wanted to scream – Oh yes, please, thank you so much. When can we start? But of course, trying to be calm, I said the obvious.

"That would be wonderful Suzanne, but it would cost a lot of money."

"Yes Lesley it would, but there is always a way. Are you busy this evening?"

"No, I will just be relaxing in the hotel."

"Well if it's okay with you, I will pop over tonight and meet you for a coffee in the foyer around 7.00 p.m. It will give us both time to think some more about such a venture."

"That would be lovely. I will wait for your call. It was lovely to meet you too, Barbara, looking forward to catching up with you soon."

"I too, Lesley, take care."

As I got in to the car, I smiled, feeling so happy and upbeat knowing that at last I have met on my trip some good and honest people. I was so excited about Suzanne's ground breaking ideas of building the country's first ever hospice for women. That night Suzanne called,

"I am five minutes from the hotel Lesley," said Suzanne, calling from the car.

We met in the foyer as I was ordering Turkish coffee for two.

"Lesley, with the experience you have until now, do you think you could build a business plan for a typical British Hospice, including layout, equipment and the staff utilisation needed?"

"Yes Suzanne, we have a well-known hospice in Glasgow. I will arrange a meeting with them and start the plan layout as soon as I get home."

"Great Lesley, it really would be wonderful to set up. It won't be easy, as most families here in Saudi Arabia believe it is only right that they themselves look after their loved ones who are terminally ill, at home or by a hired nursemaid. The subject of a hospice is rather taboo. However, through your presentations and social media, I am sure that when families have a better understanding of the benefits of a hospice, it will encourage families to go down this route, as it will give peace of mind to their loved one and all involved. The last thing I want to mention, Lesley, is that if you agree to such a proposal I will back you with a million dollars."

"What?" I said.

"Yes Lesley, it won't be enough but it will be a start and I know many people who I am sure would invest."

"Oh Suzanne, this would be wonderful; way beyond my dreams."

"Yes Lesley, you do the footwork, plans and costings and I will back you with the million dollars."

"I promise; I will not let you down."

"I know that Lesley. Now you have all my contacts and I have yours. I will start the ball rolling this end, with what permissions and paperwork are needed to satisfy the government on carrying out such a project."

"Great, Suzanne."

"I must go now Lesley, have a safe flight back to Scotland and I will call you in a couple of days."

I said goodbye to Suzanne and went to my room. Just as I opened the door my telephone rang.

"Hello Lesley, it is Bassam. Talal was saying that you didn't have dinner with him the other evening?"

"That's right, Bassam, I was feeling very tired. Is this why you are calling?"

"Well, he was complaining about it, he thought you were rude."

"Bassam, I don't have time for this. I have been in meetings all day."

"So, what have you been doing in Jeddah?"

"I met a lovely lady called Suzanne, Director of Women's projects here in Saudi Arabia. She likes my business venture idea and we are going to work together."

"Who?" he asked abruptly.

"The Director of Women's projects here in Saudi Arabia" I replied, becoming so irritated by his tone.

"You couldn't have met her," he said, with a grunt.

"Why not? And, I did," was my reply.

"Do you know who she is?"

"Yes, she is a charming business woman, who I met for a meeting in her office at her Well Being Centre."

"She is the wife of a billionaire, from one of the most powerful families in Saudi Arabia."

As he told me this, yes, I was rather surprised, however, it showed that my trust and belief in her was the right decision. She was strong, indeed, a woman of substance and the right person for the project. However, this news didn't change anything as to me she was still Suzanne, my lovely new friend and business partner and the less Bassam knew about my plans with her, the better for everyone!

On my return to Scotland I felt rejuvenated. I was going to work so hard to make this business become a reality. Arriving back to the penthouse, around midday, no surprise, Bassam was still in his bed. I called my best friend Jenny who had been spending a few weeks up in Scotland and was kindly was looking after Hamish while I had been travelling.

"Lesley, welcome home."

"Thanks Jenny."

"How are you and has Hamish behaved?"

"Oh yes, Lesley, we are all great. How was your trip?"

"It was great Jenny. Can I pop by in the next hour, to collect my wee boy and have a catch up?"

"Of course, Lesley, we are waiting for you."

As I arrived to Jenny's holiday home what a greeting I got from Jenny and my wee Hamish, who jumped into my arms and almost licked me to death. I was so glad to be home.

I told my news to Jenny.

"Gosh Lesley, how wonderful, what a great opportunity you have at last to get your project started. Suzanne sounds so lovely. With her insight of building the first ever hospice in the country, her financial backing, combined with your skills and experience, many women will become more aware, have peace of mind and so many lives could be saved."

"Oh yes, Jenny, isn't it exciting, what a difference this project could make for so many."

The next day, before I had even unpacked from my trip, I called my oncology nurse, Jean, and explained to her the business plan. A few days later I went with Jean to visit one of the city hospices, taking note of its objectives and layout. I then connected with the CEO of the Glasgow Hospice, who I am deeply indebted to for her assistance and kindness in sharing all the information she had at hand with regards to layout, regulations, staffing and costings for the Saudi Arabian venture to become a success.

Back at the house, apart from walking Hamish, I burnt many a candle working 24/7 building the project. My dining table became my working space and within a few weeks and after continual correspondence with Suzanne, I completed what I had set out to do. The plans, contacts and costings were ready and in place.

Bassam would at times peer over my shoulder looking at the plans. I realised that I had to tread the waters carefully as the less he knew, especially involving money, the better for Suzanne, myself and the project to become a reality. I am hiding the plans in a safe place because I know I am living with a time bomb, and he can explode at any moment, but I am done being one of his victims!

Our Greatest Glory is not in Never Failing
But in Rising Every time We Fall.
Confucius (551 – 479 BC)

Today, I am meeting up with Jenny for lunch.

"Lesley, I am going back to London next week. I am so happy that you have completed the project. It will give you a chance to live and get away from Bassam."

"Oh yes, Jenny, I am counting the days."

After a pleasant afternoon with Jenny I returned home to find my jewellery box, which I had hidden, now open, lying on top of my bed. All my mum's beautiful jewellery was gone.

"Oh no," I cried. All the happy memories that the pieces conjured up for me were gone. Diamonds, gold, and semi-precious stones, all gone.

Bassam was in the next room, I knew, yet again, it was him, like a thief in the night. A man without a conscience, a man who would do anything to anybody as long as there was money to be got.

I entered his room.

"Bassam, please return my jewels. Please, don't do this again. They were my mum's."

"Oh, shut up bitch, I needed the money. You will get them back."

I screamed, "No, return them now."

Hamish started barking at Bassam as he raised his hand to punch me.

"Get that mutt away from me," he said, as he went to kick wee Hamish.

"Don't you dare touch my boy," I said, as he punched me on my face and his foot hit Hamish.

I grabbed the back of his jacket as he went to leave the apartment. He turned and punched me again so hard I could feel my face swell as I fell to the floor from the impact.

Standing over me he goaded, "Talal says, Emile claims you told her you were writing a book."

"That's not true Bassam! Emile ... she suggested I write one."

"It's over. I will finish you, sharmouta," he said, while spitting on my face.

"I will make sure you never work with Suzanne in Saudi Arabia," he shouted, as he walked out the apartment door.

I was in so much pain. I could feel my eye begin to swell as I tightly held wee Hamish.

"What a good boy, trying to protect your mum," I cried.

I called Jenny, "I am on my way Lesley, stay where you are."

Jenny arrived about half an hour later, I was still on the floor. The energy had been sapped from me.

"You poor soul Lesley, look at you, your eye is bruising. Come, let me help you to get up."

I sobbed, "He has taken everything I had of my mum, Jenny."

"We will call the police."

"No Jenny, he could destroy my project with Suzanne, I need to get away before he spoils my business venture."

"But you can stay with me in London."

"I know Jenny, I love you, but I need to be independent and fulfil my dream."

"You can't stay here, Lesley, it's too dangerous."

That same afternoon Jenny called a woman's refuge centre in Glasgow.

"Come over, don't worry, we will help your friend."

In a quiet location they took us to an apartment. They were so very kind and tender as they listened to the events that had just taken place.

"Don't worry Lesley," they said. "You can stay here for as long as you need, we can help you find a way out of this situation."

"Thank you," I said, as they left Jenny and I to chat.

"Lesley, this is fine for a few days. They are good people."

"I know Jenny but I can't have wee Hamish with me, dogs are not allowed."

"We could give him to your dad for a few days and just tell him that you are going to travel for a week or so to visit friends, so as not to worry him."

"Yes Jenny, I could do that."

An hour or so passed, then Jenny got ready to leave. I too stood up and put on my coat.

"What are you doing Lesley?"

"I have changed my mind. I am going home. I can't stay here without wee Hamish. I have a business to get going. This is my country, it is my home, I will get justice for what this man is doing. Just watch this space!"

As we were leaving, the door of the adjacent apartment was open. I could see a pretty young girl, early twenties, with her mum, standing over a cradle with a beautiful new born baby girl fast asleep. We chatted for a little while. The baby's mother was obviously going through such hell with her partner. My heart was breaking as I looked at the wee bairn in the cot.

It is so very wrong. This young woman, with her baby and the many more just like us around the world need a voice. I need to be heard and perhaps someday I can bring justice for those still suffering in silence.

A woman's Tears

Be careful if you make a woman cry
Because God counts her tears
A woman came out of Adams rib
not from his feet to be walked on
not from his head to be superior over
but from his side to be equal
under the arm to be protected
and next to the heart to be loved.

By Louise (no longer a victim)

Two nights later, Bassam returned home. I heard him walking along the hallway. Hamish pricked up his ears, my heart was pounding. The footsteps stopped outside my room's door.

"Ssh Hamish, ssh wee boy," I said, as I held him hoping he wouldn't bark and that Bassam wouldn't open the door. I waited in silence for what seemed forever, until eventually the shadow from underneath my door disappeared and I heard his footsteps going further away, towards his en suite room.

"It's okay, wee Hamish; he has gone," I said, as I uttered a sigh of relief.

It took some time before I started to drift off to sleep, when suddenly yet again I heard his footsteps coming back along the hallway. It was still dark outside, what was he doing? He passed my door, pulling what sounded like his suitcase on wheels behind him. I lay silent, holding Hamish, as I heard him open the front door and then close it quietly behind him. I lay still, until I knew it was safe and he really had gone. Eventually I got up, putting on all the lights as I made my way to his room. As I looked around, I realised that a few items of clothing were missing, as was his passport. What was he up to? Where was he going?

That same morning, I went to check our penthouse at the top floor. I couldn't believe it. The apartment was empty. All the paintings, rugs, furnishings, everything was gone! Was I in a dream or was I losing my mind this can't be happening? I called all his mobiles; no answer. A few hours later I called the police. It was too late, he had disappeared! While searching his room for any clues to his whereabouts, I found a suitcase with papers and documents that just about sucked the very energy from my being.

Inside the suitcase I found mail which he had kept from me, including condolence cards when I had lost mum, credit card arrears he never paid while I was so ill, money he had borrowed from businesses and banks, that he never returned to them, electricity, council tax, factors fees, parking fines of thousands of pounds, which he never paid, letters from friends he had borrowed money from and never returned. I was numbed and for a day or two, not sure what to do.

Letters came in the mail regarding sequestration of the properties and Sheriff office letters for him to appear in court. The doorbell would ring and I would be so afraid to open the door. The phone would ring and no one would speak. Were gangsters after him for their money in the shady life he led? I felt sick to my stomach. There is only so much a human can endure and I think I have had my fill. How had all this happened? I had indeed dated Jekyll but then had married Hyde.

As I put the pieces together I realised that unbeknown to me, he had started making plans to sell everything around me while I was very sick, expediting the final phase while I was in Saudi Arabia to build the cancer foundation project. He had executed his plans very well, leaving me to fight for survival on many fronts, alone and penniless.

One week later he called me saying he was in Egypt and was sorry and that he would come back when he was ready.

"Bassam, you have left us with no home, no money. Hamish and I will end up on the street."

"I will send you £50 a week," he said, "and as soon as I am back on my feet I will send you £100,000 for a cottage by the sea, which I know had been your plans before I ever met you." I knew it was just another lie.

That same night I called Talal.

"Please, you promised to get me a house Talal, please help me. Bassam has left the country and I have nothing. He is a thief. He has defrauded my country, many commercial institutions and many people. Please help me, I am scared."

"I will see what I can do," he said.

Talal eventually sent me an email saying he had reached a decision and for the next eight months he would send me £200 a month. I gasped in horror. Oh please, this can't be true. To purchase their falcons, for the sport of kings, they will pay £26,000 but can you believe it, for a human life, a woman, his brother's wife, I am only a commodity valued at £1,600. Like so many of their women in the 21st century, I have become one of the untouchables.

The next day Bassam sent me an email:

"Why have you told Talal about me. You will be dead before I come back to Scotland, you will never get back to Saudi Arabia and I will stop you doing any business with Suzanne at the Women's Well Being Centre."

Sure enough, I never heard from Suzanne again. I ask you, what's a girl to do?

Left with such a trail of destruction, I ask myself, will it be easy being a 'Bag Lady'?

'You'll never find a better partner than adversity.'

Golda Meir (1898 – 1978)

Note to Reader:

Well obviously this was no fairy tale; the princess had certainly not met her prince, so whom had I been introduced to and then married you might ask?

What you have just read in 'Spider's Web' might have given you a glimpse, through the window, into his world.

In Greek Mythology the young Narcissus fell in love with his own image, reflected in a pool of water;

so I ask you, how lucky was I?

*Asian
Adventure*

Church Wedding Ceremony

*Wedding
Celebration*

One of the Saudi family homes

Penthouses in Glasgow

Dr Gillian (Miss Marple)

Jean, from oncology, (my angel)

My fight begins

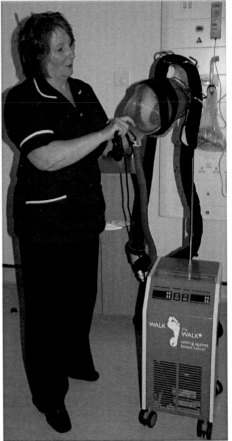

Cathy with the Ice Cap

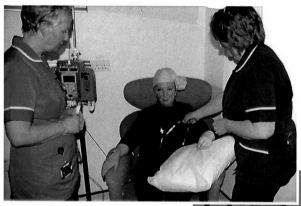

Cathy and Donna, my nurses

*Chemo over – 31 days
of radiotherapy starts*

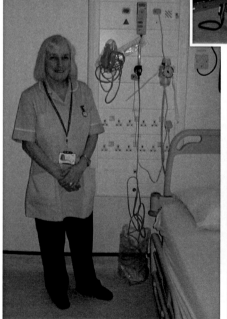

Violet (a very special Nurses Aid)

Million Dollar Deal

PART 3

Miracles Do Happen Just Believe!

Miracles Do Happen, Just Believe!

W ell, everyone, have you ever seen the movie *Sleeping with the Enemy*, with Julia Roberts? I thoroughly recommend it. Like myself, she was in a spider's web when she decided to get away and build a new life for herself. She took the decision to get on a boat; her destiny being where no one knew her.

I decided likewise, although in my case I got on a train, my destination being a beautiful coastal town, called Troon, where no one knew me.

Until Now!

What the Caterpillar Called The End,
The Butterfly Called The Beginning

It's late November, cold and wet, as I take the train, with Hamish and the few possessions that I could salvage, to my new home in Troon. It's a very small flat. From the outside it looks rather charming, like the home of Thumbelina, but the inside is so tired and damp, with one bedroom and a small galley kitchen. However, what Thumbelina lacks on the inside, the location makes up for, with its stunning beach walks and sea views, only two minutes' walk away.

As darkness fell, I took wee Hamish along the promenade to explore our new surroundings. It started to rain heavily, a gale was approaching as giant waves pushed over the sea wall. In the distance I could see through some of the windows of the little cottages and houses along the seafront. Christmas trees were already decorated, their fairy lights sparkling in anticipation of the very special time approaching. Chimney pots puffing away as log fires crackled with a gentle glow. I pictured families gathered together, sitting around their tables having dinner, cosy and snug, like a picture perfect

Christmas card of love. My heart is bleeding and aching for my beautiful mum.

"Oh Hamish what is going to happen to us? Who will be with us at Christmas, who will sit with me at my Christmas table? Oh, I've just remembered, I don't have one; I don't have a table!"

That night, after a cup of noodles, I tried to sleep on the camp bed, tossing and turning while being roughly massaged by the springs of the mattress. Hamish lay at my feet as we both gradually drifted off to the lullaby of howling winds and rain amidst the brewing storm.

Adapt or perish, now as ever
Is nature's inexorable imperative
H.G.Wells (1866 – 1946)

There are no Treasures
greater than Friends

Note to Reader:

For the next few pages I want to tell you about the wonderful strangers I would meet during my first few months in this beautiful coastal town. What precious friends they would become and what they did for me would help me to turn my life around and gain the power I once had when I had been living in Saudi Arabia.

Next morning, we awoke early. The storm was still raging, as I peered through the window at the wintery, grey sky. I got warmly dressed, with my wellies on, before Hamish and I braved the elements to survey our surroundings, in the daylight. As we walked, the rain and winds blew us from side to side and in the distance, through the mist, I could see small lights ahead. As we approached a building, I peered through the window; what a welcoming sight. A cosy fire was lit, soft lights around the room illuminating lots of books on shelves. A woman was holding a coffee pot and waving at me, with the biggest smile.

"Come in," she beckoned.

I smiled, "But I have a wee dog with me," pointing down at my wee Hamish.

"That's okay," she said, opening the door, "There is a big storm coming, like I haven't seen in a long time. Come on in, both of you, and get warmed up."

At last, we felt warm and cosy, as Hamish curled up in front of the fire and I chatted with Aida, proprietor of this quaint wee coffee shop, the Beach Cafe, over the most delicious cappuccino. My first encounter, with a beautiful soul in Troon.

That evening the storm was still raging, as Hamish and I enjoyed our first home cooked meal. We had no oven, just a hob, but that wasn't a problem. I cooked a big pot of delicious barley soup which I so enjoyed as Hamish munched contently on the tasty ham bone.

"We are safe and warm Hamish," I said, as my eyes began to close. "Tomorrow will be a big day. I need to get stronger, to walk better and find some work. I am so tired wee boy, I am so tired ... "

The next morning, yet again, we woke up to howling winds and rain. I had a good night's sleep and felt quite upbeat as I enjoyed my morning coffee and planed my day ahead. Oops, mobile ringing,

"Hello, it's Jenny. How are you settling in?" said the voice on the other end of the phone.

"Oh Jenny, it's so great to hear your voice. Yes, we are okay, but I need to find a job real quick."

"Lesley, you can't, you are still too weak. Listen, I am arriving from London in a week's time and I will stay with you for the month until you get a bit stronger with your walking and mobility. How does that sound? We can spend Christmas together?"

"Oh Jenny, that would be so very lovely."

"Okay then, that's sorted."

"The only problem is we will be rather cramped. I only have a single camp bed to sleep on."

"Not a problem, I will bring my inflatable mattress. Don't you worry, we will manage. Now Lesley, I don't want any arguments, but I have put money into your bank account. There is enough to keep you going till I get there. If you need any more or anything else, just let me know."

"Oh, Jenny ... "

"Don't cry Lesley, you are like my wee sister. You have always been the one looking after others, so take time out, it's your turn. I need you to get stronger. So relax, and explore your new surroundings. The beach is beautiful in Troon, so keep wrapped up and enjoy your walks with Hamish. You will meet new friends. It's just a matter of time before you turn everything around, remember, I know you too well."

Jenny lifted a great weight from my shoulders. Sure enough, when I went to the bank and checked my account, I was overwhelmed. That night Hamish and I had a feast. I was even able to celebrate with a wee glass of Merlot and Hamish with a big juicy treat.

It is the friends you can call up at 4.00 a.m. that matter

(Marlene Dietrich)

One night, while walking on the promenade with wee Hamish, in the rain, from a distance I could see a woman standing, with her umbrella swaying gently in the wind, and like me, out with her dog. I stopped, we chatted and we laughed as though we had known each other forever. One hour later we hugged goodbye and arranged to meet for coffee the following week, at Aida's. Her name is Margaret and any future hospital visits I had to attend, she would always be by my side.

The next day, again while walking with wee Hamish, I noticed a small van called Magic Carpets. I approached the driver to ask about cleaning the carpet in Thumbelina.

"Hello," I said to the man sitting in the van, "may I have one of your cards with your contact number for carpet cleaning quotes."

"Aye, my name is Michael, here you are."

"Thank you Michael, my name is Lesley. I will call you tomorrow."

The very next day, Michael came over to view the carpet.

"It's just a wee carpet, it won't take me long. My machine is in the van, I can do it noo."

"Oh, that would be lovely," I said. "Can I make you a coffee?"

"Aye, thank you, but I will do the carpet first."

Gosh, I was thinking, I wonder how much this will cost? By the time he finished the carpet looked like it was brand new. We chatted while he had his coffee.

"How much do I owe you Michael? You did a great job."

"Well lassie, I don't want any payment, thank you. It was such a small carpet and you made such a good coffee."

Next day, Michael arrived to Thumbelina with a woman by his side.

"This is my daughter Caroline, we thought since you had just moved in Lesley, you could do with this microwave and television, until you get yourself organised. We don't need them," he said.

I was overwhelmed, "Oh, thank you so much," I said, to my two wonderful new friends.

That same afternoon there was a knock at my door. As I opened the door, standing there was a beautiful woman holding a basket of flowers.

"Hello, I am your neighbour next door. My name is Rona these are for you. Please, if you need anything just knock my door and come in anytime for coffee."

I held her to her word. I would often sit with Rona in her home having coffee. Last week she was a stranger and now becoming a new wonderful friend, relaxing together, sharing stories and dreams, as we marvelled at the magnificent views from her window, of a never-ending ocean.

The next day, I received a call from one of my friends, Jean, who I had met while in Saudi Arabia and was now living back in Scotland.

"How are you Lesley? Are you settling into your new home?"

"Yes Jean, the town is lovely and I am meeting such friendly people."

"Are you feeling stronger, Lesley?"

"Well sort of, I am still very tired and trying to walk a wee bit longer every day to get stronger with wee Hamish. I still cannot rise from a chair, or get up from the floor, without holding on to something. The medical team believe it was because my nerve endings have been damaged by the cancer treatment. But hey ho! That's okay. At least I am still alive and have my friends."

"That is so true Lesley. I was thinking, when are you free to meet up for a coffee?"

"Actually Jean, I am going to the job centre tomorrow. I need to find work and have a CV made."

"Lesley are you sure? You are still weak. I don't think you are ready to work."

"I know Jean, but I must start earning money. Bassam has left me with nothing."

"Has he been in contact?" she asked.

"No, not since he said I would be dead before he came back to Scotland."

"So he is not helping you?"

"No Jean, both he and Talal lied, saying they would help me. Bassam even sent a text that he would send £100,000 for a cottage."

I tell you what Lesley, I will meet you for coffee tomorrow, after your appointment with the job centre, and I will bring my sister Meg along who is very professional with computers. I am sure she can help you with your CV.

"Jean, thank you, that would be fantastic."

The next day I went on the 45-minute bus journey to the city of Ayr for my appointment at the job centre. I am feeling a wee bit nervous, with butterflies in my stomach, unlike me, or shall I say a tad embarrassed being in the position I am in, as I am going to a place that I really don't want to go. However, hopefully they will be able to find me a job.

I have noticed this week that I have been a little breathless and more tired than usual, but it is probably the fact that I have had so much to do and so much to look out for. I suppose I am just not pacing myself very well.

As I arrive at the job centre, the security personnel ask to see my appointment letter before I am allowed to enter the premises. I am feeling rather lost, no one has ever stopped me from entering a building before, but I am sure there are reasons just not so obvious to me at this moment in time. I have a number and wait to be called. I so want to cry but I need to be strong.

One hears so many stories about the job centre and on the television people like me are referred to as spongers because they have no job. Well, I tell you, everyone has a story. I have overheard the plights of others. People like me, holding numbers, waiting anxiously to see an advisor, hoping that he or she will speak to us kindly and be understanding about the rough patch that has crept into our lives. Most of the jobseekers are in this position through no fault of their own, hoping for a way out, and better lives for their families.

It's Never Too Late
To Be What You
Might Have Been
(George Elliot)

Eventually my name was called. My advisor's name was Yvonne and if at any time she was not there I was seen by another courteous lady called Gina.

"Hello, Mrs Sehli, how can I help you?"

"Well Yvonne, I am looking for some work. I have just started writing a book of empowerment which will be a manual, I hope, for my future keynote speaking business. However, in the meantime I have to earn some money."

"What are your qualifications, Lesley?"

"I was an Aviation Cabin Inspector in Saudi Arabia, as well as holding seminars internationally."

"Anything else?" she said, looking rather surprised.

"Yes, I have helped to build a fledgling Scottish Airline by having crews trained for the company's two aircraft. I have also assisted in helping a family with a part of their business, taking them from the red to the black."

"Why is it Lesley you are still not working?"

"My husband from Saudi Arabia has left me destitute and I am fighting cancer."

"I am so sorry. You are going through the mill."

"It's okay, Yvonne. I have just completed two years of treatment. Because my cancer is very aggressive, I have been given everything, including a new miracle drug, called Herseptin. If I make it to the end of 2018, I will be considered cured."

"Lesley, we don't have jobs for your qualifications here but might I suggest volunteer work to start you off. I will give you contact numbers and also please visit your local council office, because as you are building your own business you can be eligible for tax credits. You have my contact number and I will see you every two weeks till you are on your feet."

"Thank you so much, Yvonne, for listening to my story."

At that moment, because of the realisation of the possibility of receiving tax credits, another seed had been sown. A new company called, Lesley Sehli International, was born.

After my appointment at the Job Centre I made my way along to the Kyle shopping centre to meet Jean and her sister Meg. It was about a fifteen-minute walk and what a cold, wet day it had turned out to be. It was such a relief to get to the coffee shop and meet up with the girls.

"Hello," said Jean, as I approached the table, "this is my sister Meg."

"Hello," said Meg, with the most lovely smile, "so nice to meet you Lesley."

Meg and I, since that day, have become the best of friends. I could say anything to her, knowing that it would never be repeated. Not only did she prepare a CV for me, but through time she would prepare all my PowerPoint presentations and would work through the wee hours, many a day, helping me to collate my book. As with Aunt Helen and Jenny, Meg would be very much part of my journey, fulfilling my dream.

A few days pass and I receive a telephone call from the council office.

"Hi, is that Lesley Sehli? This is Jo from the welfare office. Could you come tomorrow to my office and we can discuss your situation and some of the ways we can help you?"

"Yes, thank you," I said, "what time suits?"

"If you come around 10.00 a.m., Mrs Sehli."

The next day, yet again, I met a wonderful human being, who didn't look down on me because of my current situation, but made me feel so welcome. After some discussion she said,

"Lesley, from your work history, ethics and the trials you have recently been through, I know nothing is going to stop you and you will turn your life around. At this moment in time you can apply for tax credits to help you with your business and I will give you the contact number of the Ayrshire Hospice to speak to the manager of the volunteer section. Her name is Hilary, she is very professional and efficient. Perhaps there is something you can do there on a volunteer basis till you get back on your feet on your feet and build your business."

Jo, from the welfare office would become another good friend, always there to listen if and when I needed any advice. Her husband, Mark, would be the one to accompany me to the Beatson Hospital oncology unit to take all my photo shots for my presentations and my book. It must have been a little difficult for him that day, seeing so many people like me fighting for their lives, but he never flinched. All he did on that day was capture beautifully, with his camera, the sense of survival and that miracles can happen if you just believe!

A few days later, I called Hilary at the Hospice and she arranged an interview for me the following week with her assistant manager called Sandra. What an interview and what a beautiful person Sandra was. We talked, shared stories and I smiled as she offered me the opportunity to be involved with staff training, conducting my motivational training package to all the staff within the hospice. On completion of the staff training programme I was asked to conduct a talk to the business community on behalf of the 800 plus wonderful volunteers who work at the Hospice. Like my oncology team, I can only describe them as Angels without wings.

As Sandra had mentioned to me at my interview,

"Lesley, I always knew there were a lot of good people in this world, but my goodness it wasn't until I started working here with all the volunteers that I realised they were all here under one roof!"

A week or so later, while walking with Margaret, we meet another dog walker called Jack. He was the older gentleman of our group, who had so many wonderful stories to share with us about his life. We all enjoyed listening to his seafaring adventures of sailing on boats that he himself had built. He became part of this wonderful group of people and a few months later we would all find out how strong, unselfish and caring he really was.

And Dear Mollie, who is she you might ask?

Mollie is an elderly woman who uses a walking stick to get around. I regularly saw her in the distance, walking on the promenade, regardless of the weather. I so admired her for her strength and determination as she struggled through the storms; gales blowing around her, the waves spraying her as they leapt over the wall, with the odd fish or crab caught up in the sea's fury and falling onto her path. Eventually, as I got stronger, I was able to catch up with her.

"Hello, I am Lesley and this is my wee boy Hamish."

"Hello, Lesley and Hamish," she replied, "lovely to meet you. My name is Molly."

What a remarkable lady and what an adventurous life she had led. She was well travelled, had started up her own goat farm in France when she was already in her sixties, producing her own cheese and guess what, had written a book. From that day, we would often share a cup of tea together and what wisdom poured from Molly that so inspired me on my journey. A wonderful, caring soul, an absolute treasure of empowerment.

After some time, I started volunteering in Cancer Research. The team of volunteers were a brilliant bunch, working around such a great cause. It is thanks to people like them that I am still surviving and able to receive my Miracle Drug. Maritza is one of the team who helps out in her spare time.

"The book you are writing sounds fascinating," said Maritza. "You know my back ground is in media and perhaps when you have completed your book, I can get you some coverage?"

My goodness, what a beautiful town and so many positive things are now happening around me. I feel more and more empowered thanks to all the new friends that I am meeting.

My book is coming along and I have planned my first presentation in one of the small coffee shops just before Christmas which all my friends will attend. It was a wonderful Christmas time and my talks are being well received.

I think it just must be because it's winter but I seem to be more chesty than usual, or perhaps it's the dampness of the walls throughout Thumbelina. I wish I could find another flat but everything is too expensive. As the days pass I seem to be getting so fatigued. Never mind, I will get some cough mixture at the pharmacy and, hopefully, as the warmer weather arrives, I will start to feel better.

A few days later Maritza called me.

"Lesley, can I pop over? I have some good news for you."

"Sure Maritza, I will put the kettle on."

A little later she arrived to say, "Lesley, can you believe it, the flat beside me is up for rent. It is double the size of Thumbelina and less expensive, newly decorated and with no damp. I told the landlord, Andy, that you are my friend and he is giving you first refusal."

"Oh my, sounds great, I do need to move from here, the damp is so affecting my breathing."

"If you are interested; call him tomorrow."

Oh Please! Not Monsieur Cancer again?

One month later, Hamish and I moved into the beautiful flat in a listed building. A few days later, February 14th, I invite those strangers who have now become my friends, for nibbles and wine. It was a magical evening as they all sat chatting with each other in the gentle glow of flickering candles. I can honestly say that at that moment I felt on top of the world. That same evening, as I got ready for bed, my left arm started to swell. I just thought that something had probably bitten me. Next morning, as I woke and looked in the mirror, the swelling was worse but this time on both arms and my left leg. I was starting to expand like the incredible hulk.

I called Maritza, "Sorry, can't make shopping today. I am not feeling so well."

"What's wrong, Lesley?"

"I don't know, but my whole body is swelling up."

"Open the door Lesley, I am coming in."

As Maritza arrived, it was obvious she was taken aback by what she saw. I called my oncology nurse and told her what was happening.

"Lesley," she said "you must go now to the nearest hospital, before your condition gets any worse."

"Come on," said Maritza, "I will take you in the car to Crosshouse Hospital, it's the nearest to us."

As we arrived at the hospital both of my arms, legs and my face had swelled up so much I now really was the incredible hulk.

"Gosh Maritza, I hope it's not Monsieur Cancer showing his face again. I have too much to do. I need more time."

"You are strong, Lesley, you will be fine."

That same day, I was admitted to the hospital. Can you believe it my kidneys are failing! I ask you yet again what's a girl to do?

Once again, my life is in the hands of strangers. Well you know what they say 'Third time Lucky'. The team of doctors stabilised me before arranging a kidney biopsy. I so hope Monsieur cancer is not visiting my kidneys but I suppose only time will tell. I just have to believe, even if it is him again, I am ready, so bring it on. My renal physician is called Catherine. I feel so relaxed with her and I know she and the team will do the best they can for me.

"Lesley," said Catherine "we are going to move you up to the dialysis ward. Please don't worry, you are not having dialysis at this point in time. We will arrange your biopsy from there."

"Thank you, Catherine."

That week I would spend in hospital, waiting for my results. To my relief it was not Monsieur Cancer, however I have now been diagnosed with a chronic kidney disease, called Nephrotic Syndrome. Can you believe it is so rare that there are only three cases per 100,000 a year? The exact reason why it happens is unknown but the doctors believe it is linked to my fight with Monsieur Cancer.

Yet again, I have lost my hair, but as before it will grow back, third time lucky, as I have said. It is painful even to walk. Both kidneys are leaking but Catherine is hopeful that I will stabilize. That week in hospital while waiting for the results, I was never alone. Jenny, Meg and all those strangers whom I first met when I arrived to Troon arranged a rota and in turn remained by my bedside. As for the oldest member of our dog walking group, Jack, let me tell you now, why our group think of him as caring and unselfish, simply because he wrote me a letter offering, if need be, the gift of life!

"Lesley, you have been through so very much, if it becomes necessary, please accept my offer to you of one of my kidneys …."

"You See, Miracles do happen when you surround yourself with Love"

Wee Hamish

*Left destitute and
sick in Thumbelina*

Note to Reader:

Well, we are now reaching the end of my story, for now! I do hope you have enjoyed being on this adventure with me. A new journey is about to begin:

* *My book launch was on the 25th October 2016 in the Troon Library*

* *An extract from my book won Waterstones New Novice Writer Award.*

* *My story made the newspapers of the Ayrshire Post and Scottish Daily Record.*

* *Not only can I walk, but I can run!*

* *My recent nuclear scan at the oncology department is clear. The Miracle Drug is working and if I continue like this, for the next two years, I will be considered cured!*

* *My kidneys are in remission. It's a miracle; there is still not an explanation why!*

* *I am now travelling as a keynote speaker with my little book of empowerment.*

* *Television appearances are in the pipeline.*

* *A Scottish publisher mentioned it could be a movie*

So please, watch this space!

Meg and I working on the book

**It's not what happens to you in life that matters,
It's what you do about it that makes the difference!**